MAKING WAVES

the 2013 anthology of stories and poems
by members of
the Federation of Writers (Scotland)

Published 2014
by New Voices Press
imprint of the Federation of Writers (Scotland)

www.writersfederation.org.uk

ISBN 978-1-906708-16-0

Acknowledgements:

Thanks go to Eveline Pye, Nuala Watt, Mary Edward and Finola Scott for their work in sorting and selecting the works in this anthology, and to Etta Dunn in commissioning the print and publication.

Cover design by Etta Dunn, based on an image of "The Decuman Wave" by Ivan Aivazovsky, courtesy of Wikipedia.

Foreword by Carl MacDougall

For the fifth successive year these pages show that the quality of Scotland's literary voices is as buoyant, strong and varied as ever. More than one language is used with skill and humour and though some themes are recognisable, there is a readiness to tackle new subjects for a new Scotland:

> my dreams feel the red
> of that red paint
> and sometimes
> when I'm breathing
> the air feels the red
> of that red paint
> and I realise
> that no matter what I do
> or what I say
> you're never quite all gone.
> — from *Stain* by Jared A Carnie

Domestic violence gets a welcome airing alongside loneliness and disability; the ghost of debt sits with history, while our desires for travel, argument and observations of our surroundings and ourselves are still evident. Family memories appear in various forms, and, as always, the ways humanity has endured and continues to survive is celebrated:

> we are the little people
> scuffling through life
> head down, collar up
> standing at the shipyard gate
> praying for a nod
> — from *Sixty Seven Minutes* by Lesley McKay

Some of these works remind you of their origins, and other evidently early efforts rub shoulders with prize-winning pieces:

> Footsteps on floorboards come close.
> A ginger tom pulls a face at the window
> and just before you start to feel vulnerable,
> the unmistakable scent of apples
> settles your pulse; regenerates hope.
> — from *Apples* by Stephen Watt

4

And, most impressively, just the right amount of emphasis and detail is used to tell as much of the story as we need to know:

> "In your family, words like ambition and determination were hurled in accusatory tones. Cochranes had a destiny or a fate. Their deaths were dramatic and sudden. Stroke felled a few, while others choked their last at banquets... Accidents happened. Suicide was not unknown. One uncle leapt from Beachy Head. Portuguese chambermaids washed the brains of his cousin from the walls of a Lisbon guesthouse. It took weeks to patch cowardice, extravagance and folly into a plausible explanation."
>
> — from *The Chinese Picnic* by Christine Macrae

So, as we expect, writers continue to set and pursue their own agendas, and yet again this fine anthology celebrates and testifies to the mystery of why we bother to do it at all:

> They had the apparatus of speech.
> Their tongues were not prisoned.
> Did they wake one day
> to find their mouths full of words?
> — from *Inchkeith Experiment* by A C Clarke

AUTHOR INDEX

MAKING WAVES

Ingrid Lees

spring just sprung

the oldwoman
hobbling along the pavement
    admires herself in a mirror
                    where Jill Morven Ann skip
                    hopscotch and giggle
       in the sun
the quaintoldwoman
doubled over her stick mutters to herself and shivers
    when a warm wind hits her face
                  as Bruce Jason Ross race past
                  stick out their tongues and snigger
       in the spring sun
the crazyquaintoldwoman
raves something about
    bills bills bills
    heads and balls bouncing against walls
    the rent man chasing them under sheets in the back court
    a bailiff tipping dolls out of prams into the road
    and a fatherunclefellow taking her in the dark by the river
                  Ross Ann Jason Morven Bruce Jill
                  stop in their tracks and stare
                      giggle
                          snigger
                              laugh out loud
                                  and run
       in the warm spring sun

Kriss Nichol

A Breeze Of Restless September

I remember standing by the loch,
an underside of light flickering up from the water
fretting over shoreline rocks

bordering dark fields of night,
where hollows fill with mist and call to hillocks
covered in coarse pelts of grass,

and a breeze of restless September
blowing across my face in the grey before dawn,
where time belongs to no-one.

Life here is watercolour wastes
of sky, sweetness in the air, music of swollen rivers
and the feeling of being home.

The Chinese Picnic

You wrap your tuna sandwiches in greaseproof paper. June sunlight bounces from the kettle as you fill a small flask with tea. You turn the radio off and take the keys from their hook. On summer days like this, you celebrate your continuing existence by dining in the park.

A glimpse through the landing window confirms that the distance vision that has stood you in good stead for seventy years remains sharp. Having grasped the importance of dietary fibre early on, you never underestimated efficient digestion and evacuation. X-rays reveal your knees to be arthritis free. You have retained your marbles and lived a lifetime without haemorrhoids. Your cervix once evoked comment from a delighted nurse it was so like that of a younger woman. You consider cautious use of vitamin supplements important and attribute the mobility so frequently remarked upon to half a century of daily cod liver oil. You swallow calcium to ward off fractures. First a wrist, then a hip. It stretches the pension but where better to put your money than into your skeleton. Friends have crumbled away ignominiously.

When, long ago, the doctor said your health's your wealth, it was music to your ears. He could spot, he added courteously, a person who believed in moderation, who was a stranger to excess. You recall his gentle smile.

"Money can't buy a constitution like yours, Miss Cochrane. I urge you to cherish it, if only for me."

"I do take it seriously."

"And it shows. We have our well-being in our own hands. Our health's our wealth."

The slight deterioration you've lately noticed in your hearing is almost welcome.

You take your usual route through gum-splattered streets. Children skid along on scooters, boards and bikes. Toy prams and buggies neglected, three little girls have set up shop on a quilt spread over the pavement.

"Do you want to buy our toys?"

You scan the garish junk.

"I don't know any children."

"Have something for yourself, then," a boisterous girl says. "What about this?" She holds out a bangle, plastic pink and purple hearts on elastic thread. "It would suit you. It would go with that blouse."

"How much is it?"

"Twenty pence."

"Well, I'll have it."

You hand over a fifty-pence piece. The girl places it on a saucer and fiddles ostentatiously with coppers.

"Keep the change."

You are accustomed to litter and dandelions sprouting from gutters but your days of pestering councillors and letters to the Herald are over. The graffiti-splashed underpass fascinates you now. Along the cool dark tunnel, you study codes and signs. In the park, dogs sniff the shrubbery, sturdy matrons in frocks take the perimeter in serious strides, and you encounter, in your lunch spot, the Chinese picnic. Because there is such a crowd, all generations, babies sucking bottles to sinewy old men, it would be rude to sit at your usual corner. Tinfoil parcels, plastic boxes and greaseproof packages of food cover every table and much of the grass. Women are chatting, families spill beyond their tartan rugs and men are playing games. Children smile from every swing, seesaw and slide.

What strikes you is how used to merely bearing witness you have become. Last night you dreamed yourself sitting among children on a beach, waiting for a puppet show to start. You woke early, unable to obliterate the image.

In your family, words like ambition and determination were hurled in accusatory tones. Cochranes had a destiny or a fate. Their deaths were dramatic and sudden. Stroke felled a few, while others choked their last at banquets, conferences and balls. Accidents happened. Suicide was not unknown. One uncle leapt from Beachy Head. Portuguese chambermaids washed the brains of his cousin from the walls of a Lisbon guesthouse. It took weeks to patch cowardice, extravagance and folly into a plausible explanation.

Accustomed to failure, you were no stranger to panic attacks and diverse anxieties, but these have fallen away now. You outlasted them. You learned to value modest accomplishments over grand schemes and put your energy into trudging through each day, with none left over to seize the next. In no time you considered loneliness inevitable and survival a triumph.

The Chinese children are dancing. You once wanted to be a choreographer, but the whisper went unheard. You were blamed for not being tough enough, for not being tough at all. You wore your heart on your sleeve and never managed a thicker skin.

You pay your silent respects to the *Daphne* that sank on her launch in 1883, drowning more than a hundred of the men and boys who built her. By the bronze memorial ship sinking forever under her bronze river, you find a bench and unwrap lunch, acknowledging the nods of strangers with 'lovely day' and 'how nice to see the park so busy'. You eat the tuna sandwiches, two digestives and an apple, and enjoy the flask of tea, oddly refreshing on such a warm day in spite of being piping hot.

Children are playing hide-and-seek in the trees, as though they have been hiding there forever. Others fish in the pond, wielding nets and jam jars with string handles. Some have plastic boxes full of tiny fish with bulging eyes. Skilful children catch fish with their bare hands.

Toy yachts sail over the water. You stand still watching the swans. You decide to buy a piece of haddock for tea. Nobody is left to know how you reached this day, how steadfastly you prevailed.

Stain

You left
with that can of red paint
you'd got from somewhere
covering my clothes
staining the walls
emptying it on my car
and never looking back.

The clothes were washed
or thrown out
and the walls were re-painted
and the car was cleaned
and it's like
you were never here
and certainly never left
in that splashing red blaze.

But then sometimes
I swear
that when I'm talking
my words feel the red
of that red paint
and sometimes
when I'm sleeping
my dreams feel the red
of that red paint
and sometimes
when I'm breathing
the air feels the red
of that red paint
and I realise
that no matter what I do
or what I say
you're never quite all gone.

Ann MacKinnon

The Battle Of Glen Fruin, 7 February 1603

The schuil teacher tain them oot
frae Dumbarton High School
tae wutness history in the makin,
a pace collogue that birled intae dirdrum.
Baith sides came airmed and het-skinnt
fur a fecht, no ready tae transack.
The MacGregors agin the Colquhouns,
the massacre began.

The loons staundet,
fair dumbfoonert at the slauchter,
till they were roondet up and taen
tae Laf-nar-foul, the Hollow of Sorrow.
Alan Og Macintauch slew them
tho they had nae weapons — 'naked
and without armour'.
They prigged tae God tae save them
but tae nae avail.

A memorial stane stands on the sicht
but hoo mony fowk mind o the lads
felled fur just bein in the wrang spat.

Ann MacKinnon

Traisir Skills Oot

Maist o' the time I pu the strings ticht
but yaince in a while I lowse them
an a whail clamjamfray o' traisir
skills oot.

Mind thon time we strachled
tae the taimaist pint o' the ben
and gowked at the siller strath ablow.

Or yon nicht we stravaiged the links
wi nae shune and saw the gowden baw
vainish intae the grund ebb.

Whit aboot when we skited
through the opal snaw on tap o'
a haund howkit sled?

Or ran soakin through sapphire smir,
drookit and chitterin but still lauchin
fit tae burst.

Aye its lowsin time. I maun pit
the jewels back in the poke o' ma mind
and draw the strings ticht.
I'll tak them oot anither day.

Mary Nixon

Buttons

Everything's changing. Only two weeks to go at primary school. We're helping the teacher move to another room for next year's class. Mr Younger (the heidie) is going to retire. Miss McTavish is getting married — at last. My mum's pregnant (bit embarrassing) and we're all going up to the high school. I hope I'm in the same class as Sarah and Angela when we get there.

Miss McTavish says, "Thanks for moving all these boxes. It's going to be strange at the bottom end of the corridor." She's going down to primary four next year.

Big Wullie says, "Aye, we've put her aff primary seven for life."

She says we can go back and see her when we're at the high school. Wullie was out the room when she said it.

The office ladies have been going round the classes collecting money for Mr Younger for a present, so I thought — We'll collect for the teacher as well, but just for our class. Then Billy and Stevie say they're going away for their holidays before the school stops.

"Right then," I say. "I'm bringing in a tin tomorrow and you *better* have some money."

Everybody thought it was a good idea but nobody had any money 'cept for their crisp money and dinner money. Sarah found some coins in the cloakroom and kept them since it was for a good cause. Angela found a big long set of felt pens in the back of her cupboard and she had an artist's pad as well.

"We could raffle them," she said, and started ripping up bits of paper from an old jotter for raffle tickets. We just made it ten pence a go and less if they only had a few pence. The wee ones were the best. They'd buy anything, like when we had a bring-and-buy sale. They'd bring in a bag of old rubbish toys and then buy somebody else's rubbish toys.

We made over four pounds. Good, but not good enough for a nice present. We told everybody in the class to bring in money the next day. Sarah thought we should beat folk up — folk like wee Janice and Sandra — but I didn't want to lose my monitor's badge right at the very end of primary seven.

Next day I'm down helping The Jannie clear stuff out the big cupboard. There's this old toffee tin that rattles but I can't get it open. The lid is stuck all the way round with sellotape.

"What's in there, Jannie?" I ask. He shakes his head and says, "I don't want to disappoint you but it's just a load of old rubbish, been here for years. I've been meaning to throw them out for ages."

"But what is it?"

"Buttons and foreign coins. They're not worth anything."

"I know an expert," I told him. "Let me have them. You were only going to throw them out anyway. Please?" And I gave him my best smile.

"Fair enough," he said. "And if they're worth a fortune we'll go halfers and I'll go to the world cup finals."

"What?"

He laughed till the tears ran down his face and into his beard. "Joke, lassie," he spluttered. "If that lot's worth anything I'm a Dutchman."

Soon as school's over I'm running up to my granny's house. She's been watching the antique programme every Sunday for years. She read in the papers that before the cameras zoom in on the experts they are all standing about and sitting at tables with folk called researchers looking up books that tell you all about antiques.

"Call themselves experts?" says my granny. "Bloody ridiculous. They don't know any more than me. Only difference is the big fancy books they look up."

So the next time she wins the bingo she buys a book about antiques. Then she keeps getting more till she knows more than the folk on the telly.

I put all the stuff out on a tray for her to get a good look at them. The coins look nice and shiny. The buttons look like the ones my mum put on granny's blazer when she lost two on the bingo trip. She shoves the coins out the way. She goes to the drawer for her special magnifier and starts on the buttons. Then she gets one of her books out the bookcase. She starts to look up something and then she sits down sudden, all red and out of breath.

"I don't believe it," she whispers. She can hardly speak. "If this book is right then these are very rare military buttons — and I think you've got a whole set."

"What's military buttons?"

"Buttons from an army uniform from a very long time ago — that's if me and the books are right. I'll need to go and see a real expert tomorrow."

Butterflies in my stomach the next day till it's time to get out of school. I dive up the house and there's this man in a big long raincoat.

"Well, young lady, your grandmother says you found these buttons."

And I told him about The Jannie's cupboard. How he never knew where the tin came from. The man said he'd investigate and let us know what he found out. I was gutted we never got any money right that minute but next day very nearly everybody brought in money for the teacher and we got flowers. We even got the shop to deliver them. Her face was like amazed and shocked at the same time. She was very nearly crying. She says we can have a party on the last day. Everybody likes her better now that we're leaving for the high school.

Turned out the buttons were worth a fortune. The man in the raincoat told my granny and she very near collapsed with the shock. It was thousands and thousands of pounds.

My granny says, "Ye never miss what ye never had." I think that means we're not keeping the money. So I thought about when we sang for the old folk and had to go up the hill to the home cos they never had a bus or anything to bring them to the school.

"A mini bus," I said to Sarah and Angela.

"But what about The Jannie?" they said.

"He was going to throw them out anyway," I said.

So that was it decided. It was only a second hand bus we wanted but still cost a bit more than we had. The man that owns the biscuit factory down the road heard about it and gave the rest. We all got our photos taken in the home and outside the home with the old folk, The Jannie, my granny and the mini bus. It was the nice man from the Gazette that took the photo and asked all our names. Famous at last.

My granny's really proud of that bus. She says it'll probably not be that long till she gets to use it.

20

To A Mouse

Every Year we get certificates for saying a Burns poem. I always get a good mark but Janice and Big Wullie win the certificates every time. So the teacher says she'll give a prize to the best personal project about a mouse as well. See Wullie, he knows everything about Robert Burns. He knows where and when he was born and when he died. He's even been to Burns's Cottage. He knows a lot of poems as well and his grandpa wins prizes for saying Tam O' Shanter. His grandpa wins a bottle of whisky every year at this dinner and he's got to eat haggis, turnip and totties. He says that the haggis makes you thirsty and the only thing that helps is the whisky.

I told my granny and she just laughed and said, "Any excuse."

We got haggis at the school dinner but I never liked it. It was too peppery and I kept going to the well for a drink.

Everybody was bringing in their projects in the morning but the teacher wasn't going to judge them till the afternoon.

"That's no' fair," said Wullie. "How can we no' do them in the morning?"

Miss McTavish said, "That's enough William. You did very well in the recitation so I'm sure I'll get a nice surprise in the afternoon when I see your project. Just have patience."

We were getting the whole afternoon to present our projects. This is a new idea the teacher's got. You've to stand out the front at her desk and explain everything to the whole class.

My stomach was doing butterflies and somersaults at the same time but Wullie was dead confident cos he'd already won a certificate for his poem. Before he started the poem this year it was funny cos the teacher said, "Are you sure this is the Robert Burns poem and not one you wrote yourself?"

She was probably remembering that time the poet came to the school and she had to stop him in the middle of saying his poem. You never know what he's going to say next and it was quite rude.

"So, William and Janice, you will get your certificates at a special Burns assembly," the teacher said. She added, "I'm glad you're good at something William."

Wullie said, "I'm going to get her for that. She'll be sorry."

In the afternoon the teacher tidies her desk till it's empty and makes sure it's right in the middle of the floor.

"Who's first?" she says.

There's Wullie, Stevie, James, Samantha, Angela, Wee Sammy, Sandra and me. 'Cept I'm not doing it cos I forgot to bring it and my mum's away into the town on the bus so I can't even get her to bring it up.

"Me, me!" shouts Sammy. He's jumping up and down all excited. She lets him go first cos she knows what he's like with his problem with nerves, in case he wets himself again.

Sammy opens his box — a shoe box — and brings out the picture of a mouse. He holds it up to show us but it's that wee you can hardly see it.

"My mum sent it," he said. "I told her on the phone and she sent me a picture and a letter. Want to hear it?"

"No, Sammy, letters are private," says the teacher.

"And she sent me this as well. It's a mouse."

We're all standing up trying to see. It was a tiny teeny pink mouse with a white tail.

"Oh, it's a sugar mouse," says Miss McTavish. "That's lovely. You can eat it."

He puts his stuff back in his box quick and we give him a clap. I bet he keeps that mouse forever.

Next is Sandra and she's got a box the size of a coffin. She brings out a folder, books, pictures and a glass box with a mouse in it. She puts them on the table and starts telling us a million billion things — boring. I stop listening cos I can see my granny getting off the bus. This is the best seat in the class. Granny is talking to her friend Veronica. She just calls her Ronnie. Veronica's a funny name but so's Ronnie for a woman. She's my granny's bingo pal and she's got a wee Jack Russell dog called Jackie.

"What else would I call him," she says. "He's already called Jack."

Funny or what? I'm hoping she'll look up at the window.

I don't see Stevie or Samantha's projects. Sarah jags me with a pencil and Angela's bringing out a cuddly toy mouse and a wind-up mouse that goes along the table then falls off. She's got a story about a mouse as well. The teacher says that it's really good work.

Last of all is Big Wullie. The clock says ten minutes to go. He's carrying the box out to the teacher's desk.

"Last but not least," she says. "I hope this is as good as the recitation."

"It's better," he says.

He lifts the lid a tiny wee bit and brings out a ruler and two Pot Noodle tubs. He turns the tubs upside down and puts the ruler on top of them like the hurdles. Then he brings out a whistle and an apple. He puts the string that's on the whistle round his neck and places the apple carefully at the other end of the table from the Pot Noodle tubs.

"Mice are no' stupid," he says and starts telling us about all the things they can do. He tells us about every kind of mice in the world. The teacher claps so we all clap as well. Then he goes back in the box, lifts a real mouse on to the table and blows the whistle. The mouse goes flying over the ruler, the teacher jumps on a chair and Wee Sammy wets himself all at the same time. It's been the best day ever.

Alison Craig

Swan

Walking the shore early, self distilled by sleep,
new and pure in morning's thin, flat light.
A breath held between winter and spring
and the pull of the estuary like the pull of
blood in the veins, of sky on water.
And a swan makes her way from Largs
to Saltcoats, tacking across the tide,
bobbing like an empty carousel horse
or a paper boat, a prayer written
into her bows and floated away.
But a woman, I think, of an uncertain age
between youth and maturity,
where you can get away with less
flesh and more attitude.
A dirty stopout in oiled white feathers,
gaudy-mouthed, because she's worth it,
wings folded fatly, twitching into place;
she heads home after a night out
to the bleary husband who slept through
the time she said she'd be home.
Not like when she was young and
darkened her waiting father's doorstep,
some slick-eyed boy keeping to the shadows.
She sails out of sight, her wake lapping
at my feet in memory,
leaves me drinking the soft air, longing
for that quiet treaty of women.

Lindisfarne

In the footsteps of monks, I walk
wet sand like a grey mirror
sliding into a grey sea, which drifts
into a blue-grey sky.

The low dunes stand watchful, grey guardians
of this vaulted peace.

Ahead two bodies, one a reflection,
foetal, hooded, imagined reality, which I know
cannot be true.

They are an illusion, formed by the brokenness
of a tree washed bare, reclothed in green and brown
by the sea, shades of life in death.

On this half bright day, I wander
the margins of Lindisfarne
exposed, as the tide ebbs and flows,
boundaries changing.

CHROME

8:09 am

I can't hit the snooze button again. I'll just lie here for another few minutes and think about the day ahead of me. I'll think about Emma. If I close my eyes I can picture her as though she's standing in front of me. Her glossy brown hair hangs loosely, framing her slender, oval face. Her skin has that year-round natural glow; she swears it's natural and I believe her. She has eyes that look like little pools of dark chocolate rimmed with thick, dark lashes. Her nose has the tiniest of bumps along the bridge, which only adds to her beauty. Her lips are full and curved and have the most perfect Cupid's bow. She is nothing short of mesmerising. On the bedside table my phone goes off. BUZZ BUZZ BUZZ BUZZ! Christ, it's like the world, or at least the company, cannot function without me.

I pad through to the bathroom; there is nothing better than the feeling of the carpet on your bare feet. I step into the shower and think about how this day will change my life.

10:17 am

I've always been successful, as far back as I can remember. I was very quiet but observant at school; even at five years of age I was happy to sit and listen to my teachers, to learn what they had to teach and to put it all into practice. I sit at the breakfast bar in my kitchen with a cup of black coffee and two slices of brown bread toast. I think about my mother. I wonder if she'd be proud. Throughout my childhood, she just patiently watched and encouraged me. I was never any good at team sports. My younger brother loved playing outside; tennis in summer, football all year round. But not me. School didn't really help me to become more outgoing and sociable. I liked solitude. I wonder if my mother worried.

My phone starts to ring; it's the office again. I let it ring off.

From my stool, I glance around my flat. Simple and modern, it really does suit me. The sun shines in from the window behind me, giving the living room a sepia glow. It creates warmth and homeliness that, in reality, probably don't exist here. It has always seemed to me that people fail to appreciate simplicity. Everyone wants clutter; their homes, their lives. They don't make it easy. At the age of twenty-four I started up my own computer logistics company. I kept it simple. By the age of twenty-seven I made my first million. It was all very

26

simple. I kept my life and my business clutter-free. It has always given me clarity.

I start to clear away breakfast. I wipe a cloth across the breakfast bar; the chrome top is shiny and perfect. The sun has moved, just ever so slightly, but enough to change the room. It no longer has a warm glow. It doesn't look like a picture from an old film any more. It looks simple. It is clutter free. It looks cold.

11:43 am
I can remember the first day that I ever saw Emma. My company had begun to take off, I was making enough that I could now afford to employ a few people. The office space was small. I had spent the evening before reading through replies to the job ad I had placed for an admin assistant. I didn't have a specific person in mind. Someone quiet and efficient who could get on with the work I gave them to do. A little after nine in the morning she bounced into the office. She was so far from what I had imagined I would have alongside me every day. She was bubbly and enthusiastic and it was almost infectious. It is hard not to like Emma. She got the job. She was efficient and quick but she also brought exuberance into the place. She brought me coffee every day just the way I like it. She designed a filing system for me that was easy to follow and simple. She made me laugh. She held my hand the day I buried my mother. I fell in love with her.

At the end of each working day, we were always the last two left; filing the last of the paperwork, sending those final few emails. She would come to me then, calm and happy.

"Do you need anything else, Callum?" Her voice is sweet; it has a certain musicality about it.

"No thanks, you can head home anytime you like."

Thinking now, I can be too strait-laced; there is never room for error, no margins to relax a little. She lingered around the door sometimes, watching me. It took me a long time to realise why.

"We should get a drink sometime, relax a little. Sometimes I feel like I hardly know you."

She smiled at me and left before I had answered.

I have a few hours before I have to be at the church and I argue with myself about whether I have time to go for a run. You see, I'm worried that if I don't go for a run I'll have a drink instead. I feel as though every nerve in my body is exposed and shaking. My insides are wrung so tightly I need a way to ease them apart. Emma usually does that for me. I definitely don't have time for a run. I'd have to shower all over again. I pour a whisky and drink it neat. I feel its warmth spread through my stomach. I pour another, just for good measure. It has done its job. I feel calmer.

13:27 pm
I want to call my brother and tell him about today. I can't. The words are there, in my head. I just don't know how to bring them out. He probably wouldn't understand me anyway, he never has.

My buzzer rings; it's the florist. I sit down on the sofa and open the box. It is tied with a beautiful light blue ribbon. In fact it's almost a shame to open it. Under the lid there is the most delicate sheet of tissue paper. She has put thought into every detail. I look at the rose I will wear as my button-hole; every petal is flawless, there is not a blemish to be seen. It is the most brilliant white colour. It is perfect. I had expected nothing less.

My suit is charcoal grey. She told me so many times how much the shade suited me. I suppose I am quite attractive to women. I pull on the crisp white shirt, buttoning it up slowly and with care. Every stitch I will wear today was made for me. Like everything else, it must be just right. My shoes, only the finest Italian leather, are polished. I pick up the tie, emerald green, her favourite colour. If I could cry, I probably would. I fasten it around my neck, measuring it out perfectly so it will hang just right. I pull over my waistcoat and fasten it. I am binding myself together.

The electricity is starting to hum through my body again. Nerves are jangling. I sit down on the bed. The Egyptian cotton is soft and soothing under my fingers. I can hear my phone; I must have left it in the kitchen. It is ringing, louder every second. A warning bell, it is dinging over and over. I don't want to speak to them. I don't care what the problem is. Do they not understand what today is? Nothing will be the same now.

I lift the rose from the box with careful gentle hands. It really is a perfect flower. I pin it to the button-hole and I smile to myself. I pull on the jacket. I am ready for her now. I am perfect too.

15:00 pm
The church is beautiful. The altar is decorated with dozens of white roses, just like the one I am wearing. The people are all dressed in their finest. I look at Emma's mother; she is preoccupied, smiling at the people around her. The sun

is pouring through the stained-glass windows. She got the day she deserves. She was so worried about having a September wedding with all the rain and bad weather. She needn't have.

There are hats and hair-pieces of every shape and size and colour. The men are all in smart suits. I can see Emma's sister, holding her two-year-old by the hand. Little Isabella looks like a princess. I smile. I look at my watch; it is almost ten past three. People are starting to fidget. The priest takes his place. A quiet consumes the congregation. My stomach is doing somersaults, the electricity is buzzing so loudly it is all I can hear. Then I hear it, the first note of Wagner's Bridal March and everyone stands. Every head turns to face the door at the back of the church, anticipating the arrival of the bride. At that moment all I can smell are roses. The electricity dies to a quiet hum as the organist plays: 'DUM DUM DAH-DUM; DUM DUM DAH-DUM; DUM DUM DAH DUM DUM...'

I see her then, walking towards me. She is smiling as if her life depends on it. Her face is so beautiful and joyful. My heart leaps in my chest. And she walks, slowly, steady, each step very precise. Each step she gets closer. She looks straight into my eyes then and smiles. I feel like I might collapse.

I stand there, in the second row and watch as Emma glides past me. All I can see is the back of her head, her veil. I watch as she stands on the altar, before God, before me and everyone else in the room, and says those words. Not to me, the man who has loved her since the moment he first saw her bounce into his office. To another man, a better man. Better because he did what I didn't. He saw the chance and he grabbed it. I didn't. I couldn't. The words were there, I wanted to say them so many times. But I didn't. Instead, we worked. She brought me coffee every day and designed a filing system. All the while I said nothing. We never went for that drink. I never took her up on the offer. By the time I realised that there was a chance, the window had closed. She didn't hang around waiting for me. Rightly so, I suppose.

I sat at my desk, I held my meetings and closed the deals. Except for one, the only one I really wanted.

The congregation starts to clap; many people have tears in their eyes. I hear them mumble to their neighbours about how beautiful and perfect the service was. Emma is crying as she walks past me, hand-in-hand with her husband. She is truly radiant, the most beautiful bride I have ever seen. And she is happy; I can see that too.

29

Miner's Son

He had the power o' life and death,
yon man wi' the hard black hat.
Ye worked at the face, or above ground,
but only at McEachern's word.

Says he, "Yer boy's due oot the school.
Fetch him here on Monday
and we'll stert him at the pit."

"Na-na," says I, "it's an apprenticeship for him."
Robbie was fourteen and filled wi' laddie's dreams.

"Eh, whit?" McEachern cries, "Awa' wi' ye!
There's a joab fur him ootby."

Weel, McEachern has his say and I hae mine,
but in the end he smiles his foxy smile,
"Man, bring the laddie here next week, or
bring me ower the door-keys tae your hoose."

He had the power o' life an' death,
yon man wi' the hard black hat.

Syne Robbie stertit at the pit.

Amy Anderson

Tortoiseshell On A Gatepost

Stretching up
to a raindrop,
he is a bottled garden
of moss and winter ferns,
a plunge pool of brown trout
and kelp, an armful
of minnows and silt.

Home

He remembered it all very clearly. It had been the mid-fifties when they had made the decision to put his mother into the home — the lonely tour of a hollowed-out stately home with its musky boxes of rooms, metal-framed beds on wheels, tiny windows too high to see out of, bibles at the bedside tables. At the time, he'd been a young businessman with only the week-ends free, and had thought to take her into the little cottage that she herself had encouraged him to buy. He'd always intended for her to live with them one day — had visions of her stooping over the chicken coop with a handful of feed, singing old songs from his childhood with her sweet yet piercing voice; but his wife had laid down the law. When the subject of losing her home came up, his mother had not wanted to cause a fuss, but he knew how terrified she was of old folk's homes — care homes — whatever they called them, it made little difference to the reality: a room she would never leave.

She hadn't left it either, not after he had taken her on that early excursion to the rose garden, fitting her fragile ankles onto the wheelchair foot-rests while she clucked and whimpered at him, asking confused questions to people who weren't in the room and warbling 'Jerusalem' in her quaint little voice. He had experienced a rare flash of empathy for his mother then — the full reality of what was about to happen to her sinking in, her big, grey eyes scanning the tiny room for signs of life. People had died in the spot she now sat in, staring at the mottled ceiling, listening to adverts for Ice Cream and Miracle Gro as their vision began to fade, knowing that this was the end of existence.

In spite of her little illnesses and moments of foolishness, his mother had been a very clever woman. She would know where she was and what it meant. Not even she was strong enough to resist the dreaded midnight realisation that this was it — that death was coming — that every load of washing, every goodnight kiss, every chuckle at her child's curious face had been leading up to it. She had sat on that awful leather-effect chair, her old head appraising the walls, the bed, the vase, the TV and radio, the two bags of clothes for the nurse to hang up once she 'got settled'. He remembered how her smile had gently flickered from her face, her hands clasping and stroking her handbag as if it were a faithful dog. A terrible smell had emanated from the hallway as he opened the door to leave — it was dinnertime.

What kind of reward had entry into that godforsaken place been? Of all the things he could have done to repay her little kindnesses — the new suits she had bought him when his business was struggling, the support she gave when his wife left him, all the little favours that rose from love alone — he had made only this single dumb gesture of defeat, signing her into a book alongside the names of dying people, condemning her to a cell to await extinction. He still couldn't think about that without crying; the blank look of panic she had cast at him as he finally backed out of the room, asking if he really *must* be going now, some part of her brain still lucid, still aware of how uncomfortable *he* must feel, not wanting to make a fuss about it.

She had quickly spiralled off into a land of her own creation after that. With each visit she was less interested in the world around her. She refused to leave her room, howled and screamed at the slightest suggestion; yet the room had nothing of hers in it, nothing to keep her there but her own will. She had destroyed everything she owned, giving her clothes and books to charity.

Well, it wasn't going to happen to him. He'd die first.

"Now now Mr Smith, what have we told you about keeping your hands off that IV tube? It's very important not to take it out, isn't it? Yes. Very important. This is what's making you better, see? See?"

"Save your breath, Helen. This one doesn't have a clue what's going on."

David Betteridge

A Second Home

Picture this:
Aeneas fleeing Troy,
salvaging his most dear.

His little boy
he tows behind him by the hand;
his father, frail burden,
he carries piggy-back;
images of household gods,
wrapped in his cloak,
he clutches to his pounding heart.

Behind: the ransacked city, red
with the work of Grecian swords,
and loud with the boast and ruin
of their war.

That's Hecuba, bereaved, allotted now
to Odysseus as his victor's spoils.
That's Cassandra, raped last night,
foreknowing evil's rule;
she is Agamemnon's prize.
And that's Andromache... and Creusa...
They, and many, many more, cry
in the flame-filled air.

Entrapped with them,
as Troy falls, we hear their pain;
we track Aeneas as he crosses miles
and leagues of enemies and seas;
we watch him plant the seed of Rome.

Our convoys there are poets' words.
Reading them, we give the ancient deaths
and lives they tell
a second home.

David Betteridge

Graffiti Generations

Carved on a stone wall:

"FOR EVER":

an old love's declaration — whose? —
its words outwearing lives.

Now, with our chalks and sprays,
we in our new-born thousands pass,
and do the same.

The weathered stone-cuts blur.

Love, recurrently re-named,
survives.

The Book

When the knock came
she held her breath and waited.
Late morning in a strange place and
broad daylight for God's sake.
'Who is it?' she whispered, trembling.
'I'm from the government,' he said.
A wave of panic swirled in her head.
'One moment, please.'
Where the hell had she put that book?
She'd have to look, make it swift
no sweat, keep her cool.
Conceal the evidence below the bed,
no, under the mattress would be best.
Throat sealed with fear
she undid the lock,
slid back the bolt,
opened the door.
'I'm here to fix the telephone.'

Angela Blacklock Brown

Working Girl

Just after seven she drifted
into the bar, midriff bare,
wearing scarlet shorts and crop top,
young, careworn, painted doll,
lipstick laid on thick,
cheeks rouged like a circus clown,
liquid eyes, lost look of a downtrodden dog
wandering around tables, trying her best to
chat up disinterested men intent on
drinking beer, watching each move
in the football match on giant TV screens.
She leaned over, whispered,
'My kids need to eat.'

Bad News

It could be said that Jimmy Mitchell was not so very bad. Indeed, the committee had often said much the same thing themselves. He was a good family man, a trier, a doer of unpopular but occasionally necessary deeds. But now he had gone too far, and they'd decided they had to kill him.

It was the first committee meeting they had ever held without him, and as they sat in a semi-circle around the faux-pine table Jimmy's absence pulsed angrily like a missing molar. Every space seemed subconsciously shaped to fit his ample bottom. Charlie coughed uneasily, reading and rereading the muddled agenda he had scribbled on a torn envelope. He turned it round in his hand, flattened it out, squinted at it, waiting for something to turn up. They were always waiting for something to turn up.

"Well? Whit's the crack, then?" said Wullie. "Are we gonnae get started, Mr. Chairman?" Wullie was a jovial bear-like man, with a smile that jutted out his bottom jaw. He gave Charlie a nudge with his elbow which almost slung the little chairman along the bench. Charlie rubbed his arms with paint-speckled fingers.

"Well, if we're no' waitin' for anybody else, we might as well make a start." He glanced around. "Diz emb'dy know emb'dy who's no' comin'?"

"Aye." Stevie, thin and tall, hands folded behind his head, back so stiff it looked like a workman had propped him up against the chair and forgotten to pick him up again. He smiled an enigmatic v-shaped smile. "Ian's pickin' his boy up fae the Beebees. Says he'll try and make it alang efter that."

"Alright. Half-a-dozen's enough tae be gittin' oan wae." The light fuzzed in its plastic overhead. Someone had economically left off all the other lights in the clubroom, so that the long rectangle disappeared into darkness in both directions. An old pool table marked the edges of unstrained visibility. Charlie swivelled around in his seat to look at it.

"That pool table's a pure waste. Whit's-is-face — the boy who put it in —"

"Rocky," Wullie prompted.

"Aye, Rocky — he says he might as well take it away if it's no' makin' any money. He only goat thirty quid oot it the last time."

"Here!" Ally sat up, his blue eyes flashing open like a doll. "That cannae be right! Thae wee lads, ah see them playing it every week!"

"Who?"

"Och, ye ken them." Ally fluffed his white hair and stared at them monolithically, an Easter Island statue topped with birdshit. "Hedgie's laddie and his pals."

"Aye, but are they payin' for it?" Stevie nodded sagely and turned his eyes up to the ceiling. A knowing grin settled on his face, like he had all the answers to the world's problems. Charlie silently unravelled this clue like a threadbare sweater.

"Whit! Is somebody giein' them it for free?" His glance dashed from person to person. "How can they be gittin' it for free?"

Big Wullie stretched his arms out in a pantomime of casualness and checked an imaginary watch.

"Well, ma tea's waitin' for me, so any chance we can get on to the matter at hand?"

"Aye, aye." Charlie tried to shuffle the papers in front of him before realising he only had one. "Right. We've called this meeting the night tae talk aboot Jimmy."

Ally struggled up in his chair. "Well, ah think…"

Wullie half-raised his flat hand from the table like a drawbridge. "Ah think all discussion should go through the chairman." He settled back in his seat, interlocking his hands over his shirted stomach complacently. "Mind, that's only wan man's opinion."

Ally nodded. "Aye, right enough. Oan ye go, Charlie."

Charlie chucked the agenda onto the table, trying to dismiss it.

"Right. So, you aw ken Jimmy's been makin' an awfy lot of mistakes lately. He forgoat tae register Davis fur the Scottish Cup — that cost us two grand…"

"Aye, AND got us chucked oot," Ally lamented.

"Aye, and that… And there was that business wae the minute's silence…"

They winced in collective recollection.

"Daftie told half them it was a minute's applause," Ally muttered, still stunned. "When the ref blew his whistle and half the away end jumped up and started gein' it laldy, ah thought that wis it, the whole stand's gittin' chucked in the swanny, an' us wae it."

"Aye, then when we calmed everybody doon an' Mrs. Dorricott had stopped greetin'…"

They had tried again for the minute's silence. Forty-five seconds of it had elapsed when Jimmy's wife stuck her head out of the clubroom door. *Jimmy! Jimmy! We're aw oot of sausage rolls!* The seismic might of Jimmy's head lashing up from his mobile phone carried all the way through his body, snapping him up onto his stubby little legs with an almighty bellow: *BETTY! KIN YE NO' SEE WUR HIVVIN' A MINUTE'S SILENCE!*

They sat in expressive hush, the memory of that moment settling like dust around them. Charlie bounced his hand on his knee thoughtfully.

"Aye, so there's that. An' then there's that time wae the molehills…"

"The lawnmower parts…"

"The toilet door…"

"The insurance…"

For several minutes they passed Jimmy Mitchell's name round like a gigantic parcel of grievance, each torn layer revealing a fresh one, a Wagnerian lament of tragedies, dodgy dealings, good works become undone. A misshapen idol began to rise in their midst, messy handfuls of mud which merged into a bipedal lump.

"It's no' even that that bothers me," Ally said, cutting off all previous discussion with a swipe of his hand. "Ah'm no' fashed aboot him makin' us look like a laughing stock, or aw the money he costs us. Whit diz ma heid in is how he diz aw these things an' then he sidles up tae ye wae that stupit wee grin oan his face tae tell ye how there's been 'bad news'! As if he's nowt tae dae wae it!"

They murmured in communal recognition. It was like a pre-emptive wake, remembering him as if he was already dead, waddling across the beer-stained carpet with an opened letter in his hand and reverent glee on his face. *It's fae the S.F.A… It's fae the cooncil… Ah don't know if ah should tell ye… It's no' very good news at aw…*

Wullie's voice came from so deep a place that you couldn't imagine it started inside him. When he opened his mouth, it emerged like the echoes of prehistory.

"Right, we already know aboot aw that. Question is, whit are we gonnae dae aboot it? We aw know there's nae point daein' anythin' else till we git him oot the door." There was a pause. "We've tried shuttin' him oot, we've tried forcin' him oot, we've tried gittin' him to resign. Nothin's worked. We're aw agreed oan that?"

"Without a doubt." Ally nodded over his folded arms.

"Right. Somebody's put it tae the committee — an' ah dinnae ken who it wis — that we should jist kill him. Noo, ah don't know how everybody feels aboot that. But, tae ma mind, unless somebody else has goat a better idea, we might as well talk aboot it." Wullie gave a tiny shrug of his giant shoulders. "It

40

might turn oot no' tae be practical. Bit it costs nuthin' tae talk aboot it." He settled back into his seat like a rock being rolled over the entrance to a cave. "Noo, ah'll be honest wae ye — ah think it's probably a bit ae a last resort. Bit maybe that's where we've goat tae. Whit diz everybody else think? Sorry, Mr. Chairman." He gave a little bow of mock deference and rolled his shoulders towards Charlie.

The chairman blew his reddened cheeks out and gazed round.

"Well. First things first. Ah mean, whit would we be talkin' aboot daein' here? Likesay, wid we be daein' it ourselves, or gittin' somebody else in tae dae it fur us? Whit do you think, Robbie?"

Robbie wriggled in his seat wordlessly, trying to free up a logjam in his oesophagus. He was fat and pale, as if he had been inexpertly carved from lard, with milky blond curls sprouting from his head like grass from a potato.

"Ah-ah-ah think it's somethin' we definitely need tae have a wee think aboot. Ah mean, ah know he dis his best, but, well, pit it this wey, whit else kin we dae? Ah-ah-ah don't think WE should be daein' it, though, jist tae save a few bob. It's jist gonnae wind up costin' us mair in the long run, like when Ian and Wullie tried to pit in that radiator."

Wullie laughed good-naturedly. "Aye, ah hid ma eyes opened fur me that night, ah'll tell ye! Mind, ah wis only pittin' it in cos Stevie hidny hid the chance yet."

Stevie's folded hands crept to the top of his head, the corners of his mouth inevitably following. "Ah'm sure ah wid've goat aroon tae it eventually," he said drily.

"Aye. Aw-aw-aw ah'm sayin' is, though, it's no' somethin' we kin jist hiv a wee go at."

Ally nodded his head. "If a job's worth doing, it's worth doing well," he said brightly.

"Ah-ah-Ally's spot on." Robbie's glassy blue eyes floated fishily in his immobile rubber face. "Plus, if we git somebody in tae dae it an' they make a mess ae it, it'll no' be oor problem."

Charlie furrowed his brow.

"Eh? Martin, you're the teacher. Is that right enough, it'll no' be oor problem?"

Martin, startled, cast a quick look around. His features converged doubtfully towards the middle of his face.

"Ah'm an *English* teacher."

"Aye, bit ye'll have read a book aboot it or sumthin, will ye no'?" Charlie deadpanned.

Martin added his laugh to the general appreciative chuckle. "Well, ah'm nae expert, but in books an' that folk can still go tae jile fur attempted murder even if they jist telt someb'dy else tae dae it fur them." He wrinkled his nose and loaded his 'Thoughtful' expression. "Probably you could git in trouble jist fur bein' here when we talked aboot it."

Ally's chair-legs made a scraping noise as he shot to his feet. "See ye later, boys!"

There was a fresh batch of chortling as Ally lowered himself back into his seat, his forearm resting along the chair's back. Martin glanced up at the clock.

"Right, look, we're obviously no' gonnae dae it ourselves, so kin we no' bother wae the usual two-hour spiel aboot it? If we tried tae dae it ourselves, it'd wind up wae aw *us* deid an' Jimmy spendin' the life insurance oan tartan paint an' watter wings fur sparrows."

Wullie laughed. "They'll no kin tell the difference wae Stevie. He's half-deid as it is! Somebody haud a mirror up tae his face, the shock'll finish him aff."

Stevie's eyes crinkled with concealed merriment. "Don't you worry aboot me, boys, ah'm daein' fine."

Charlie rumpled and unrumpled his agenda, significantly making a single oblique mark on it with an old biro. "Right, if we're aw agreed oan that, we'll no' need tae bother wae a vote. Diz anybody know how much it costs?"

Ally nodded. "Aye, that's gonnae be the clincher. It's aw aboot money, in't it? Aw comes doon tae money."

"Ah-ah-ah've goat a few pals'll know, mebbe even git ye a good price. Ah kin ask aroon, if ye like."

Charlie shook his head. "Naw, it's Stevie normally gits the quotes in, come tae think of it. Stevie, kin we leave that wae you tae get a quote..."

"Three quotes!"

"Three quotes, an' get back to us?"

Stevie forced his gummy eyes open only as wide as his thin-lipped smile. The irises, barely visible, slid into the corners of his eyelids. With an indistinct noise he adjusted his hands minutely behind his head.

Charlie glanced up at him with a little nod of satisfaction, then lowered his eyes to follow a tracing finger down the torn envelope.

"Right. Noo, aboot that pool table..."

At that there came the sudden rush of noise pouring into the room through a thousand tiny portholes; beeping and vibrating, cheery ring tones, staticky sound effects. They all glanced at one another. Jackets were found, pockets emptied, screens switched on; and there, in the night, while the moles tunnelled patiently and the lawnmower turned to rust, into half-a-dozen private spaces came the half-a-dozen prophecies, "BAD NEWS..."

Our Place

Day dawns with a wind from the west
and clouds that sit halfway down the hill.
How long, my dear, have we known this place?
Let's say more than forty years, to be safe,
forty years, four decades, five hundred months near enough,
and the weeks and the days and the hours
must accrue uncounted, for calculation
adds little to the balance of life's experience.

Things seen and done add to memory,
are shuffled like cards in a pack,
come to the top in ways we can't determine.
Remember this then: that here we stand,
together, once and forty times, and this remains.

Colin Will

Fimbulwinter

Winter gave way to wan and weary winter,
seeds stayed stubborn in the stone-hard earth,
snow flakes fell in a foul and freezing air,
ice rimed ridge and rig and runnel, snow
packed hard in folds, fields and shadowlands,
and the mires of missing summers.

That was the start of it; my kin starved last year
and I sailed south, cut free of sea-ice,
and slipped down the long loch to leads
of open water, and the sea roads to lands
I hoped were warmer. We made landfall on an island
my forefathers' folk settled and tilled,
parks for the beasts, wheelhouses for shelter,
but friendship and kinship would not sustain us.
No feasting, for famine had struck at the homes by the shore,
and most had moved on, as I would at sunrise.

Coastal sailing, by headland and bay, not lodestone nor stars,
and inland the sight of white hills, lands locked in ice-grip
of the Frost Giants. Sons of Ymir, daughters of Freyr,
send greetings to Thor, we need his hammer Mjöllnir
to break the glass of this cold and to strengthen poor Sol.

(In Norse mythology, Fimbulwinter, three consecutive winters with no intervening summers, comes before Ragnarok, the final battle and the Twilight of the Gods.)

45

Linda Atterton

Seam

Do you remember the mine, Jim?
Do you remember the mine?
The last slice of the sky,
the last taste of the rain,
the clang of the cage door,
the cram of the men,
a mad dive of the heart
as we plunged into the earth,
the wet shine of its bowels,
the damp stink of its breath.

Do you remember the mine, Jim?
Do you believe we really left?
I can remember your eyes, Jim,
I cannot picture your face.
Your eyes were the only candles
God ever threw in that place.
A spark of danger,
a flicker of fear.
The echo of death,
the shout of relief.
Love was the ash left behind.
Fragments all that we took.

Do you remember the mine, Jim?
How can we ever get out?
Do you remember my name, Jim?
Or did you stand in the daylight
and throw it away?
Do you sometimes dream you're still there, Jim?
Do you sometimes look at the sun,
then carefully close the curtains,
knowing it will never be real?

46

Sandra H Brown

Britannia Panopticon Theatre

Slowly peel the layers of city dirt and grime,
reveal what's hidden underneath.
Open the doors, take a step into a bygone age,
centuries of dust, cigarette smoke,
forgotten music, lost voices, destiny beckons.
Artists trod the stage, Stan Laurel, Marie Lloyd,
Jack Buchanan, Harry Lauder, it's rumoured
Cary Grant was here too, stars of the silver screen
came here when ships were built on the Clyde.
Tuppence was paid to see something a little risqué,
pantomimes performed by Dan Leno under his
guise of Aladdin's Widow Twankee, animals
were kept and put on display, waxwork models
became part of social entertainment,
men in uniform came to forget their woes.
Slowly the music begins to fade, it's almost
the end of the decade, destiny beckons, the
stage door has finally closed, adieu to
all who came, who saw and performed.
Slowly reveal some of the layers, clean
up the dust, open the windows, open the
doors, step inside, music plays once more.
It's a new beginning of another decade.

(The Britannia Panopticon Theatre is the oldest existing music-hall in Glasgow.)

Banquo's Ghost

Shug's feet were killing him. He was wearing the best pair of shoes he'd had in a long time — practically brand new, the woman told him — but by God they nipped. He was so taken with them it'd been a while before he'd noticed that anything was wrong. Up and down the high street he'd paraded for hours, right up until Tam had caustically informed him that they were women's shoes. Shug hadn't let on, but suddenly the tightness across the laces made perfect sense, and the fact that his foot felt like it had been crammed into a poster tube became the fault of the shoe, not the wearer. So grateful was he for the revelation that he hadn't even asked Tam, as he customarily did, what cologne he was wearing that morning. By the time the smelly bastard had struggled, hissing, to his feet, Shug would usually be halfway down the road, dead on for reaching the Asda before the bin men did.

Well. It didn't matter that they were women's shoes. Shug had binned his old ones soon as he got out the charity shop rather than carry them around with him all day, so that was that. Anyway, he didn't mind. He still quite liked the new shoes. The little flecks of pink were so dark you could almost call them maroon. Maybe he'd start telling folk he was a Hearts supporter. Or a transvestite. It'd be a long time before he saw that kind of money again, and if it was a bad job, ach, he might as well make the most of it.

Having said all that, though, his feet *were* killing him. It wouldn't be so bad if he could just have a wee sit-down from time to time, but usually he was lucky to get a skelf in his arse before someone was discreetly moving him on, having pretend conversations with their walkie-talkie in order to avoid further discussion. When he sat, cross-legged, on the pavement outside Greggs, every now and again a customer would anonymously send him out a coffee in a polystyrene cup. This Shug appreciated, but by God he'd have appreciated it a helluva lot more if they'd thought to send him out a foldaway chair instead.

Nup. He limped to a gradual halt at the side of the pavement. He'd had it. Not a step more. His pain centres, perfectly calibrated, had stopped him exactly one pace before permanent damage. Pleased, he gazed around, looking for the solution. There was bound to be one. A problem wasn't a problem without a solution.

So, first things first. He could always take the shoes off and go barefoot. It wasn't ideal, but it would do for starters. He worked a lot better when he knew he had a Plan B. Relieved, he noticed he had stopped right outside the entrance to the community centre. Behind a Perspex panel a corkboard flaunted its bewildering array of youth groups, night classes and local announcements. But what day was it? Shug reached into his pocket and fished out the charity shop receipt. 19th September. His gaze rattled along the posters. Please God, anything that's on today. He didn't mind. Church group, piano lessons, anything! Anywhere he could sit down and take a load off without getting hustled by a wee chanty wrassler in a hat. That was for him.

And then he saw it, floating above a clip-art picture of some flowers: ADVANCE SCREENING... *19th September, 2pm, all welcome... The Arcady Film Festival is proud to present an exclusive advance screening of Charles Atkinson's ground-breaking new piece, 'Banquo's Ghost'... There will also be a special Q & A session with Charles after the performance... Nibbles and drinks beforehand.. Entrance free, donations...*

He'd read enough. Steeling himself for the effort, he limped up the stairs, through the foyer, and straight into the main hall.

The first thing he noticed was that it wasn't as big a deal as the poster'd made it sound. About sixty seats were laid out for a crowd of around thirty people, most of whom were huddled round the buffet at the back. Up front, they hadn't even bothered to get the big screen up on the stage; instead, at seat level, they'd set up one of those wee portable screens Shug's teachers used to use for assemblies. At a table nearby, a man with a grey ponytail was busy propping up the projector with binders so that it pointed more or less at the screen. The whole thing, Shug had to admit, did not inspire much confidence. But there was always the buffet.

"Ach, well! This is awright, in't it?" Shug rubbed his hands together and picked up a paper plate. "This'll dae fur me! Bit ae grub an' a wee film aboot ghosts? Ah'll take that any day ae the week!"

He glanced around for a response, but none was forthcoming.

"Nae takers, eh?" he chirped, heaving a clump of sandwiches onto his plate, "Quite right inaw! Git some scran doon ye, eh? That's whit we're here fur!"

As he threaded his way around the unbudging bodies, he listened in, wherever he could, to the conversations that were taking place. He could normally get interested in just about anything, but when he heard a fat woman tell a bald man in a jumper about 'a bold interplay of nature, narrative and guilt' for the sixteenth time he decided he'd had enough and went to sit down. Plumping for a chair in the back row, he set his plastic flute of orange juice down on the wooden floor and munched his way through a slice of quiche, watching the man with the grey ponytail with interest.

"Y'awright there, bud?" he asked, raising his glass. "Cheers, eh?"

The man looked up from the Apple Mac he was now fiddling with and stared at him in something like amazement. Shug, used to provoking such extreme reactions, casually took a sip of his orange juice and sighed.

"Let me know if ye're needin' a haun," he said, turning his attention back to his sandwiches. "They hings are a right bugger if ye've no' goat the knack."

The man with the ponytail blinked a couple of times, shook his head rapidly, and went back to work. Shug, turning a sausage roll in his cheek like a gobstopper, watched the overhead screen display with interest.

"Nup," he announced through a mouthful of pastry, "ye've awready looked there. Is it a film ye're lookin' fur? Mibbe it's in the wan cawed 'Films'?"

The man looked up at him again, as disconcerted as before. He turned away, took a deep, cleansing breath, and double-clicked on the folder named 'Films'. Sure enough, first item on the list, 'Banquo's Ghost'. Shug nodded in satisfaction and tossed a vol-au-vent into his mouth like it was popcorn.

"Right, is that us ready to start?" A thin, angular woman with a bob tottered to the front of the hall clapping her hands. "Okay, can we have everyone seated, please?"

As the buffet crowd started filing into the seats, Shug noticed with minimal self-consciousness that none of them had brought their plates with them. Once he was sure that nobody was going to sit next to him, he put his own food daintily on the chair beside him.

"Okay!" the woman shouted, unnecessarily. "Thank you all for coming! Now, I'm sure..."

Shug prised the shoes off his feet and placed them carefully, side by side, underneath the chair. As he wriggled his toes, painfully at first, he noticed that the woman was making frequent reference to the pony-tailed man who stood beside her.

"Now, as you all know, Charles is one of the most celebrated moving-image artists working in the field today," she bellowed, her voice echoing all around the chamber, "so I can't tell you what a pleasure it is to have him here with us for..."

Shug sat up in his seat, momentarily impressed. So that wee guy was the director! No wonder he looked so stressed out. Shug locked glances with the perspiring filmmaker, who seemed physically incapable of looking away, and chucked him a conspiratorial wink over the assembled heads.

"So, enough of me rambling on," the woman smirked to an appreciative smatter of chuckling, "and without further ado let me present the world premiere of Charles Atkinson's ground-breaking new work, 'Banquo's Ghost'!"

As the woman sat down and a ripple of applause ringed the room, Shug took a bite from his sandwich and clapped his free hand on his knee. He was no snob; in fact, in cultural terms, he liked to think of himself as something of a renaissance man. He'd give anything a go. As the lights dimmed and the whispers settled, he slouched down into his chair and prepared to enjoy himself.

Well, it was unlike any film he'd ever seen before, he could say that much about it. For a start, there was no music, except for wind-chime effects and those wee cymbals that Buddhists clink on their fingertips. There was no story to it either, far as Shug could tell, just loads of long shots of fields and shrubberies, as if somebody had left the camera on by accident. He'd noticed lots of other mistakes too, like a couple of times the film had went all blocky and faded out so that there were two images on the screen at once, like a double-exposed film. He had laughed, briefly, at a shot of somebody falling over into the snow, but then the same thing had happened ten times in a row and nobody else there had laughed even the once. He glanced up at Charles, who happened to be looking at him at the time, and winced sympathetically. Charles stared at him with a blank expression and then turned quickly away, his hands clasped tightly in his lap.

Then, after a while, and with no apparent ending, it was over. Shug started applauding enthusiastically as soon as he was sure it was finished, a raucous clatter which drowned out the polite palm-tapping from the rows ahead.

"Aye, that wis rare, that, win't it?" he announced loudly. "Aw the snow an' that, eh? That wis crackin'!"

Single-handedly he kept the applause going until the woman got up again, Charles rising shakily after her.

"Thank you, thank you!" she said, raising her hands. "Thanks very much to Charles for what I'm sure we can all agree has been a *transcendent* experience. Now, there's a lot for us to talk about there, and I guarantee it's raised lots of questions, but I wonder if Charles can get the ball rolling on our Q and A session by telling us a little bit about the inspiration for the film?"

Charles's stare plunged helplessly into them, doomed already to lock eyes with the stranger at the back of the room. Shug gave him an encouraging smile as he stepped forward, his gaze straining to break away like a spaceship trapped in orbit.

"Well, the original idea for 'Banquo's Ghost' came from a conversation I had with a friend..."

"Oh, aye, aye," Shug nodded in approval, "That's, eh, good, that, in't it."

"We got onto Shakespeare and Macbeth, obviously," Charles swallowed heavily, "and we talked for a while about art, and the art, the very dramatic art, of living..."

"Phew!" Shug puffed out his cheeks in thought and stared into the distance. "Ma heid's birlin' wae aw this, by the way."

He was trying to help put a brave face on it, but if he was honest, Shug had had just about enough. The whole thing had been an absolute shambles, there was no two ways about it. He'd got the boy his round of applause, fair enough, but now that his plate was empty and his stomach was full he felt no further obligation to the assembly. He wasn't quite ready to put his shoes back on — his toes were red-raw — but he'd go barefoot for a while. It was fine. He got to his feet, brushing some crumbs from his lap as he did so, and picked up his shoes in one hand. As Charles watched him in unmistakable horror, he sidled out of his row, apologetically pointed at an imaginary watch, and waved goodbye.

"We'd been talking about the subtle beauties of the world, the unseen, as it were," Charles went on uncertainly, "The things we look at every day and never notice..."

Overhead, the lights hummed and flickered back into life, Shug's parting gesture of gratitude towards his hosts. Charles tried to shield his eyes from the glow, the rows of faces in front of him suddenly clear and blank. In the silence a door slammed, and then another, and a piercing trill carried a tune into the distance.

"Hearts, Hearts, glorious Hearts..."

52

Just Like That

His nerves never showed. Wiry hair poked out
from underneath the fez, dressed in his best tuxedo
like every other show before.
Peers cheered from the side of the stage floor.
The audience tittered. Camera operators
examined their picture, as a spectacular blonde
helped adorn him in a gold cloak.
The theatre brimmed for the killer joke.

Without warning, he slumped; crumpled in a heap
against the velvet curtain. Uncertain laughter
greeted the magician — master of the prankster,
jester of the television;
until his twitching leg flickered the orchestra to life
and the country whispered nervously during the intermission.

Laura Guthrie

The Landscape

The gold in the blue, with the blue, is the blue. Faraway gulls cry against a backdrop roar of pitchless foam. Warm wind rustles.

Dandelions bend as shade sweeps the daisy-spotted plain. The grass is thick and glossy, feather-soft and water-cool. Clouds smell like fields.

Beach grass tops the crest. Stems sway like a curtain. Sand merges with hard, wet bronze, and waterline rivulets resurrect and subside with every tide. A blue-black wall rears, glistening, over echoes of past-broken waves. Farther out the undercurrent shifts and laps.

White tips throw salt past towering monoliths and thin veils, into a sky which dwarfs, illuminates and glorifies all the land, and soars upwards forever.

Holy Cows

Arriving near twilight
I know why they are Gods.
Lumbering black

cloud-floating white
Raven Cow, Dove Cow.
I find a biro, not

the instrument I want,
fumble two sketches.
Enough to say afterward

that I was there
in the darkening sky,
that I followed their bones:

scapula, femur, patella,
moved towards better grass
with my ancient musculature,

became visible in the
repetition of drawing
as we did in the caves.

Future Imperfect

O oh. My head feels like a cobbler's last. No more tequila slammers for me, I resolve. Why does a miserable morning have to follow a really good night out like shadows behind brilliantly sunlit faces?

I try to moisten my desiccated lips with a parched tongue. I'm in desperate need of my morning cuppa. I get up shakily and stumble through to the kitchen. My sixteen-year-old son is sitting at the kitchen table staring at his laptop. He looks up as I stagger in.

"Hmm. Looks like you had a boozy night. There's fresh tea in the pot."

Normally I would take sweeteners but this morning I feel the need for sugar, so I add a heaped teaspoonful to the large steaming mug of milky tea and take a sip.

"The postman delivered that this morning." Stewart points to a large brown cardboard box sitting on the worktop. "I didn't notice that it's not addressed to us until after he'd gone."

I peer at the label — Mrs Violet Valavanis, 10/2 Mercat House.

"It's OK, I'll take it up later," I say, watching my hand shake as I try to lift the mug of tea. I hold it with both hands and down the lot. "I feel awful. I'll have to go back to bed."

Smiling, Stewart mocks my voice: "You only have yourself..."

I put up my hand. "To blame. I know." I shamble off to crash on top of the bed.

I'm sitting on the rocks beside a high waterfall. I hold out cupped hands, collecting the pure clear water. I drink. I feel the water flowing from my stomach, through all the tissues to my skin, where it leaks out, and I'm parched. I dive into the pool, a plant wraps around my foot like a rope. I try to untangle it but it wraps itself around my arm. My lungs are bursting.

I waken with a start, heart pounding. When I try to stand up my head hurts like hell and my legs are like jelly. I hobble into the bathroom.

I sit for a long time after I've finished peeing. I can't get up. I don't want to get up. I'm quite comfortable here — could sleep here. I close my eyes. My head's spinning, making me feel sick. I must make a move. I take the bathroom stool into the shower and sit under the warm, comforting spray, letting it rain down on my hair and naked body. After a while, I reach for the shampoo.

I put on my big white towelling robe and make my way to the kitchen. My inner time clock is now completely wonky. I look at Stewart's open laptop — 18.30.

"I'll be fine after a cup of tea," I tell him.

He takes the hint.

I look at the box on the worktop and feel guilty. "I will deliver you—just let me get myself together."

"You'll what?" asks Stewart.

"Nothing. I was just thinking aloud."

"Ah. Thinking, is it? I thought I heard some rusty cogs grinding."

"Right! For your cheek, you can carry that box upstairs."

"Not me. She might ask me in."

"We'll both go. You carry it to the door then you can disappear."

"Okay. No bother."

"I'm beginning to feel a bit better. I think I could eat a bit of toast."

"Right. Toast and tea it is for the soak."

"Watch it, young man. You're cruising for a bruising."

"Help, ma wee mammy's gonna beat me up," he utters in falsetto voice.

I laugh at the sight of his six foot two inch frame cowering in mock terror, but laughing hurts. "Ouch. Hurry up with that toast and tea," I groan.

About an hour later, I'm finally ready.

Stewart lifts the box. "I wonder what it is."

"Don't be nosey. It's none of our business. We just have to make sure that it's delivered."

Outside 10/2 Stewart gives me the box and hurries away. It's quite heavy. I hold it against the doorjamb to take some of the weight off. The door opens as far as the chain will allow. Mrs Valavanis peeks out.

"Yes?"

She obviously doesn't recognise me. I've seen her in the lift a couple of times — a small slim woman with long black hair tied back in a ponytail — in her sixties I guess.

"Hello Mrs Valavanis, I'm Rosemary Ross from downstairs. This box was delivered to me by mistake. It's for you."

"Oh yes, I've been expecting it. Come in, come in."

I carry the box into her living room and carefully put it down on the coffee table.

"Please, sit down and I'll make us some tea. Do you have a headache?" she says, inspecting me closely.

"Yes, how do you…"

"It's your aura, dear. There's a break right there," she says, touching my head above the right eye where the pain's at its worst. "Not to worry. Nothing that can't be fixed. What do you take in your tea?"

"One sugar and milk please."

I sink into the soft velvet cushions of the plush wine-coloured sofa and look round the room. It's neat and sort of retro, like its owner. The window is draped with heavy velvet curtains that match the three-piece suite. They're pulled back into brass tiebacks. I can see the moon — a large yellow orb in a clear midnight-blue sky. I wonder why she hasn't closed her curtains.

She comes back with a tray and puts it down on the coffee table. Two bone china cups and saucers and a small plate holding a variety of biscuits sit on an embroidered tray cloth. She hands me a cup and saucer.

"Help yourself, dear."

I take a wafer biscuit.

"Thank you very much. I needed that," I say, having finished the tea in two gulps.

"Plenty more in the pot," she says, taking my cup and refilling it without asking. This time I sip it with a bit more decorum. "I expect you're wondering what's in the parcel," she continues.

"No… Well, I am a bit curious."

She goes into the kitchen, comes back with a serrated knife and splits the parcel tape, opens the box and removes a thick piece of foam padding, then hands together, almost as in prayer, she reaches in and reverently brings out a perfect glass sphere. I'm intrigued. I don't know what I was expecting but it certainly wasn't this.

"Would you please lift out the base and sit it in the middle of that table?" She nods her head, indicating a square table in front of the window.

I do as she bids, placing the heavy base in the middle of the black chenille tablecloth. She comes across, leans over the table and slowly opens her hands allowing the glass ball to slide gently into place.

"Now I'm at one," she says, sitting down, eyes fixed on the crystal ball.

I sit down at the other side of the table.

Several minutes pass; I see the image of the moon reflected off the curved surface. She seems lost in thought. I don't like to interrupt her but my head's still aching and I need to get home for some painkillers.

"I didn't know that you're clairvoyant," I say, breaking the silence.

"I'm a Waterbender. It's good that we have the full lunar strength tonight," she says cryptically.

"A Waterbender? What's that?"

"I heal by manipulating water."

"How does that work?"

"I redirect the chi paths in the body using the power of the Lunar Source. All of the elements have Benders — Earth, Air, Fire, Water — they're all connected. The Source influences all of the waters of the Earth. I'll show you, but first you must drink a large glass of water. I sense that your cells are depleted."

This is starting to get a bit scary—all that stuff about chi and the moon.

"It's okay; please don't go to any bother. I have to go. My son will be in shortly for dinner."

"It's no bother and it'll only take a minute. Surely your son won't grudge you that if it's going to make you well?"

I could hardly dispute this, so I take the glass of water she offers and down it as fast as I can. She brings a Bergère chair and places it facing the window, giving her room to walk all round me. I look at the face of the full moon. It reminds me of the Creamola Foam advert with the man in the moon smiling. Mrs Valavanis is moving her hands above my head — not touching. I start to relax. Maybe this healing thing's not so bad after all. She comes round to the front. She's waving her hands above my head again. Now she's bringing then down both sides and back up to my head. She repeats this movement getting faster and faster. She looks like she's doing the Locomotion. I suppress a giggle.

"Let it flow," she says in a soothing voice. "Let it flow, release that energy."

This is too much. I burst out laughing and can't stop. Tears are running down my cheeks, my nose is running and I'm going to pee myself any minute.

"I'm sorry, do you mind if I use your bathroom?"

"Not at all, that's good. That's the toxins coming out," she says.

This makes me worse. I run to the bathroom. After all the mumbo jumbo healing my tummy muscles are aching, screaming at me to stop with all the laughing. I check my image in the mirror before leaving the bathroom... That's better. At least I've washed off the Cheshire-cat look. A few deep breaths and that's me — ready to face the Waterbender. I crack up once more. Why did I have to think of that name? Visions of U-bends and P-traps pop into my mind and I have to go again. Stress incontinence I guess—maybe I'm getting to that age. The thought of it sobers me up. I compose myself and unlock the door.

"Thank you very much, Mrs Valavanis. I feel better now."

"Call me Violet, dear. I'm glad you're feeling better. Has your headache gone yet?"

"Actually... Yes, it has," I say, surprised to find that, apart from a few tummy twinges, I feel fine.

"Good, good — oh, wait." She cocks her head to the side and holds her hand to her ear. "I'm being told to give you a warning... Be careful on the steps," she says, opening the door to let me out.

"Oh, don't worry. I don't use the stairs. It's the lift for me. Bye Violet, and thanks again," I reply.

Back in the flat, Stewart is playing loud thumping music in his room. I shout to him to turn the music down. He switches it off and comes into the kitchen, where I've started peeling potatoes.

"So?"

"What?"

"So, what was in the box?"

"You'll never guess."

"I know, that's why I'm asking."

"I'll give you a clue. It's round and you get them at fun-fairs."

"A carousel?"

"No, Dumbo. Think. Something clear and round."

"A goldfish bowl," he says triumphantly.

"Close. A crystal ball."

"You mean the kind fortune-tellers use?"

"Precisely."

"So Mrs Valavanis is a fortune-teller?"

"No, she's a Waterbender."

"A what?"

"A Waterbender. She heals, using water and the moon."

"You're winding me up."

"No, it's true, she healed my hangover."

"Don't you think you'd have been better by this time anyway?"

"Maybe, maybe not."

"Come on — you? Forever the sceptic? Do me a favour."

I tell him the whole story. The bit about the Locomotion cracks him up so much that he has to use his inhaler.

I climb up the kitchen steps to get a new packet of salt from the top cupboard. On the way back down I slip, losing my balance. My right foot lands with a thud, twisting my ankle, and I'm careering backwards, arms flailing, knocking the flour and milk off the worktop. I end up, sitting in a pool of milk, surrounded by a cloud of flour and with a heap of salt from the burst packet lying on the floor beside me. I look at my son, look back at the salt, take a pinch and throw it over my left shoulder.

Second prize winner of the inaugural Federation of Writers (Scotland) story competition in 2013.

A C Clarke

Leap

Earth, moon-crescent against endless black,
curves under his outstretched foot as he
launches into deep trust: science and luck
both. Ground comes rushing up in a hurry
of welcome. He somersaults in freefall,
straightens, pulls the ripcord on a glissando
through backlit air. Fields, highways, bridges all
the well-known man-marks lay themselves before him
in slow prostration. Time to breathe easy, yield
to earth's persistent tug, drift treewards, skim
the branches, saunter down: everything held.

A C Clarke

Inchkeith Experiment

How must it have been, learning the island,
the huge sky, so often barred with steel,
its hanging lights too high to touch?
They could not say 'the grass is like...', 'the sea is like...'
or grasp the messages waves smuggled in,
the shores of Fife remote as El Dorado.

They lived in each other's presence,
their days one bright blur of sight, smell, taste.
Perhaps, like looking into a silvered mirror,
they saw each other clear, the world they lived in
framed by absence. Perhaps, like looking into rippled water
they saw a hint of likeness forever

failing to resolve. Though they heard nothing
from the woman who tended them, her throat
locked since birth, they heard from gulls,
whose klaxon swooped at them out of the air;
patrolling oystercatchers swore at them;
sheep called their lambs to order: an island babel.

As, puppyish, they chased each other,
they made some noise surely?
They had the apparatus of speech.
Their tongues were not prisoned.
Did they wake one day
to find their mouths full of words?

Mathematical Papyrus

If seven maids with seven mops swept it for half a year...
this civil servant's reckoner would find the answer
shouted in red. Want to find out how to measure
the slope of a pyramid, want to know
if fattening a goose goes faster if you coop
the bird or let it peck in the yard? This scroll's
your bible. How much beer for a workforce?
Stop at sheet three. Go to sheet five for the bread-count.
No problem too trivial, none too thorny,
from force-feeding a goose (did they eat *foie gras*?)
to calculating the area of a circle.

Just buy this scroll and you'll know all the secrets —
anything not included not worth knowing —
if you want to be high up on Pharaoh's rollcall.
Whatever you do don't lend this scroll to rivals —
not even in the next life: make sure it's buried
along with all the things you'll need for the journey,
hang on to it for dear life, like grim death.

Tough if some tout flogs it to a tourist
after buying it himself from a dodgy tour-guide
aka tomb-thief. Let's hope by the time that happens
the gods have twigged your talent and you're safe
in eternal Thebes with all the time in the cosmos
to count your geese, your firkins, your loaves of bread,
dream up mathematical puzzles for Osiris.

The Red Centre

The sound of silence. It was the first thing to strike me. That and the searing heat. It was mid-winter in Australia, but here in the outback the temperature had reached the high-eighties Fahrenheit. My companions and I spoke in low voices from sheer awe at the vastness around us.

Out of the coach to stretch our legs, a film of red dust covered my white trainers, and my socks were unlikely ever to be washed free of it. Setting aside that minor inconvenience we were treated to the unique sights and sounds of the outback. The gigantic carpet of desert that surrounded us was broken here and there by a patch of arid scrub. The jeering laugh of a kookaburra occasionally splintered the silence.

At that time, in July 1972, the only means of crossing the outback was by coach, jeep or campervan. The Stuart Highway, which today runs through the centre of the continent, had not yet been constructed and the more recent rail track to transport people on *The Ghan* hadn't even been thought of.

I was halfway through a year's working holiday in Australia, something pretty rare in those days, and my friends back in Scotland thought I was mad to venture so far from home.

On holiday from my secretarial post in Melbourne, I'd travelled to Adelaide to begin a bus tour. I was a lone Scot in a coach-load of Aussies.

Our trip took us north from Adelaide, stopping at the town of Whyalla, before we headed into the desert. In no time at all, the coach windows were powdered with dust blown around by the hot desert wind.

It was late evening when we arrived at Coober Pedy, 526 miles north of Adelaide and the largest opal-mining town in the world. In our hotel water was rationed; the contents of our basin had to be used for washing both self and laundry.

The name Coober Pedy comes from the Aboriginal word, Kupa-Piti, meaning 'white man's hole', an apt name as a high percentage of the town's miners live in 'dug-outs'. We were given the opportunity to visit these underground homes. They are serviced by all mod cons and on entering you are hit by a wall of cool air since the temperature below ground remains static.

Tourists coming out of a 'dug-out' at Coober Pedy

During our day at leisure in the town, I purchased a milk opal at one of the mines. Much later, the stone was inserted into a gold pendant, a piece of jewellery I treasure to this day.

Journeying north next morning, I peered through a partially dust-free area on the bus window and sighted what looked like a patch of water. But it turned out to be a mirage, the first of many that I would see during the remainder of the trip.

Late afternoon, having stopped for tea made in a billy by our tour guide, we entered the Northern Territory and the Simpson Desert.

A more desolate, uninhabitable terrain would be hard to find, which made the discovery of a clump of wild flowers the more remarkable. Named after an early explorer, Sturt's desert peas poked their delicate red heads through the wilderness, refusing to die.

After an overnight stay at Victory Downs homestead, we all piled back on to the coach. Flocks of budgies flew overhead, escorting us through their habitat. There were no cages for them in their country of origin. With neither humankind nor habitation, this world belonged to them and us alone.

Paddy melons were strewn around the sand, in size and texture a cross between a melon and a grapefruit. How they got there remains a mystery to me to this day. One brave traveller in our party cut into a paddy melon but screwed up his face at its bitter taste.

That afternoon we attended an Aboriginal corroboree. We, the visitors, all sat in a semi-circle on the sand with the cast facing us. The performers wore body paint, which made them a bit intimidating. They let out chants while their bodies gyrated to the sound of the didgeridoo. The noise boomed out across the silent land and I expected people to spill out of the emptiness at its command.

Aboriginal Corroboree

That night we stayed at Curtin Springs. This homestead, within a day trip of Ayers Rock and The Olgas, is a working cattle-station, run by the Severin family who took over the pastoral lease in 1956. In 1972 things were quite primitive. Nowadays, Curtin Springs offers accommodation with both powered and unpowered camping and has a pub and a store.

Curtin Springs Homestead

The following afternoon Ayers Rock, the dun-coloured monolith, now known by its Aboriginal name of *Uluru*, seemed to rise out of nowhere. Some of our party climbed to the summit of the rock, others flew over it in a small plane. I chose the former method, but my attempt was unsuccessful because the surface was smooth, with few footholds. Despite my failure, our tour guide gave me a badge saying 'I climbed Ayers Rock'.

In the evening the lowering sun edged its way over the rock, turning its smooth surface to a luminous crimson colour. We rose early and witnessed an encore at dawn when the rising sun burned away the blackness of the night and turned the rock red once more.

Sunrise breaking over Ayers Rock (Uluru)

Continuing our journey, we travelled sixteen miles west of the rock to view 'The Olgas', Aboriginal name *Kata Tjuta*. Of these thirty-six domed rock formations, Mt Olga is highest at approximately 3,497 feet. Further north and thirty miles west of Alice Springs, I stood beside Standley Chasm, dwarfed by the grandeur of the giant edifice. I craned my neck, trying to see the top of the two gigantic stone columns that soaked up the sun, leaving the narrow gorge between them shaded and at parts in deep shadow.

Standley Chasm

Our journey ended in Alice Springs. Established in 1872, the town, equidistant between Adelaide and Darwin, is overshadowed by the MacDonnell Ranges.

Alice Springs from Anzac Hill

The town was named after an English resident, Lady Alice Todd. Today the town boasts 25,186 residents, which is 12% of the population of the entire Northern Territory.

The Flying Doctor Service, so vital for the sparse outback population, began in 1928 and was started by a Presbyterian missionary, Reverend John Flynn, who'd worked with the Australian Inland Mission (A.I.M.) since it was established in 1912. Reverend Flynn became known as 'Flynn of the Outback' on account of his work with the Flying Doctor Service.

Royal Flying Doctor Service in Alice Springs

The service still operates today with bases in Adelaide, Perth, Darwin, Brisbane and Sydney and provides emergency and primary health care services for those living in rural, remote areas of the country.

One of the emergency airstrips in the outback

The trip through the Red Centre is one unique to Australia, and the memories of my time there have remained fresh in my mind over the succeeding forty years. I have never re-visited the area as nothing could ever compare with my first experience of the outback.

Catch Dreams, Add Hope

Catch dreams, the unattainable, the rare.
Seize stars of gold, grasp rainbows in the air.
Delve for diamonds in dust.
Dream the sweet smell
of hyacinths purple as sunlit swell
of summer seas in lifting mist...
With gifted visioning
glimpse mer-people, hear seal-folk sing.
Lucent melodies bob and toss
on ebbing tides.
Ah, dream of loss
and heal deep wounds.
Then dream
stillness green as moonlit gleam
of apples hung on quiet trees.

No barrier to fantasy
or extravagance. Dream a zumba dance
through maze and rose-garden,
towers of glass, high guarded fence.

Add hope to the melody —
this beat will set soul music free.

Ann Rawson

Piano

She clacked the keys like dominoes;
clicked her fingers
in neat rows —

performing that chinoiserie
called *Chopsticks*.

Mechanical, she faced the task
with crab-like hands
and rigid back.

She hammered out the sound as loud as
heavy metal tracks.

But when she finished, as she bowed,
her hair swept down,
a golden cloud —

a glittering glissando.

Ann Rawson

Topkapi Gardens, Istanbul

A glimpse
of green tapering wings
long tails
erratic flight
to and fro
in and out
of plane trees
exotic shapes.
Parrots in Topkapi.
Like
snatches of memory
lost in the leaves
of the mind.
Green nostalgia.
Never to catch on camera
what flies.

Orientation

Eyes as black as wells propel
him forwards.

Cantilevered legs
        zig-zag
                through grass
    and leaves.

He's following a strict magnetic setting,
An atavistic list of scents and needs.

And still he slips and scrambles
to the water   searching for
the gap   between the reeds.

until he stops;

winds down the spring

and quivers:

like a compass
settling in.

Different Strokes

M iss McGlinchey strived to see her teaching work as a vocation, but today it had been a trial. She watched from her classroom window as the boy left through the school gates, trailing after his father. He did not look quite so cocky now. Outside her classroom door, she could hear the clank of the metal bucket against the corridor floor and the soft swish of the mop as the cleaner moved throughout the empty school.

Miss McGlinchey looked at the clock on the wall. Quarter to four. She had better get a move on or there would be no steak pies left at the butchers. Her mother liked a steak pie on a Tuesday. It was one of her few pleasures left in life even though she never ate the crust and nibbled at the meat. Their wee dog, China, wolfed down what was left. Then, after the washing up, mother and daughter would walk up Abercromby Street to confession at St. Mary's. A huge stone angel with outstretched wings flew across the front of the church, gazing upwards, ignoring the tenements below.

The journey there was a right trauchle as the old lady had to stop frequently to catch her breath. Inside the church, the flickering light of the sanctuary lamps and the smell of incense soothed her. The kneeler squeaked as she knelt fingering rosary beads until it was her turn to visit the confessional box. Week after week, year after year, she would repeat the same sins.

There was a choice of two priests — a young one and an old one. More often than not, she heard yawning from the other side of the grille, no matter which box she chose. The young priest would try not to yawn but he never could. The old one would stretch his lantern jaws and exhale slowly, finishing off with a croak.

A shadow appeared behind the frosted glass window of the door of her classroom, followed by a knock.

"Come in," she said.

The door opened and the head teacher walked in, along with a blast of bleach from the slick floors outside. Mr. Gilhooly looked dapper in his smart houndstooth suit and gold spectacles. His moustache and beard were clipped carefully. He looked like a member of the cabinet. She half-expected him to pronounce that war had been declared. Instead he shut the door and smiled. Miss McGlinchey's stomach lurched. Then she remembered that she was not the one in trouble.

"Good Afternoon, Miss McGlinchey," he said, standing with his hands behind his back. "I gather you have had a particularly trying day."

"Yes, Mr. Gilhooly. Things have been eventful." She heard her voice break in the middle of the sentence. She dug her nails into her palms. There must be no crying — this was their first conversation since her appointment back in August.

"The situation has been resolved," he said.

For a second she wished that she had ignored the boy's drawings. That she had not picked up the greasy-covered catechism and examined the drawings on the frontispiece.

"I am sorry that I was out when the incident occurred," said Mr. Gilhooly.

Miss McGlinchey smiled weakly. Her leg still stung. She could see the boy looking up at her and his palms parting as she had swung the belt down. She could hear the hoots and jeers from the children. There had even been foot-stamping until the teacher across the corridor had appeared and taken the boy away.

"What is happening with the boy?" she asked.

"Expulsion. It will be Borstal for him. What did you do with the drawing?"

"I tore it up and threw it in the bin. The cleaner has emptied it."

"Ah," murmured Mr. Gilhooly, stroking his beard. "Where is his desk?"

"Over there, Mr. Gilhooly. Just next to the bookshelf."

The head teacher walked around the desk, examining it, before flipping up the lid. The inside of the lid was covered in drawings, incised into the wood. Deft confident lines.

Mr. Gilhooly frowned. "Mmm... Quite the little primitive. I doubt they teach medical illustration where he is going."

Then he paused for a moment. "I have something for you, Miss McGlinchey."

His voice sounded strange as if his shirt collar was too tight. Slipping his hand into his jacket pocket, he pulled out a brown paper parcel and laid it out on the desk in front of her.

She picked it up, undid the string and parted the paper to reveal a Lochgelly tawse. It was handsomely made in tan coloured leather with two tongues.

"Oh, thank you, Mr. Gilhooly, but I already have one. My predecessor Miss McErlain left it." She pointed to a strap which hung from a nail on the wall.

"Ah, Miss McErlain. She ran a tight ship. Well, until..." He cleared his throat. "This is a challenging school. You knew that when you took the job."

Miss McGlinchey nodded. She had heard of Miss McErlain's spectacular exit wearing a straitjacket.

"This belt makes a better noise. More of a thwack. Frightens the wee blighters more," continued the head master.

He smiled slowly at her. "You can call me Ignatius, my dear. And I, perhaps, can call you Theresa?"

Holly and ivy, daffodils and tulips. Christmas carols and May hymns. Miss McGlinchey could see her name on the Deputy Head's door in cursive script: Miss T. McGlinchey — on paper edged by pinking shears.

"Of course... Ignatius."

"Just one thing, Theresa," he said, moving towards her.

"Yes?" she said.

"You might want to practise your belting technique." He stretched his arms straight out — parallel to the floor, palms up, before placing his right hand on top of his left...

An hour later, after the head teacher had left the building, Miss McGlinchey saw him stop to chat to the janitor at the school gate. Collar turned up against the autumn chill. Hands firmly set in pockets.

The children had long since departed, and the street looked desolate and bare. Leaves rustled up and down the gutter as the street lamps came on.

She turned around and replaced the old strap on the wall with the new one, stuffing the old one behind some squares of felt and pinking shears in a shortbread tin and putting it at the back of the paper-cupboard.

The hands of the clock struck five and she put on her coat and slid her hatpin into her cloche hat.

All the steak pies would be long gone. But there would be no yawning in the confessional box tonight.

78

Aileen Paterson

Two Days

How delicate your unsung hands,
your purple feet pedalling air,
your soft cheek as I stroke you,
soothing your anger to
a still moment
of surprise.

You blink in the new light,
blue eyes screwed up
against the day.
I hold you close.
You find easily the buried part of me,
your murmuring breath severs me.

What a small warrior
you are.

Gillian Shirreffs

Lazarus

he returned
a summer lighter
a millennium wiser

we prowled
in opposing circles
hunting familiar souls

I tried
to spy deception
in ice grey eyes

he looked for clues
in mirrors
edged blue

orbiting
closer
we collided

ink black
he glanced
my shin

melting into grass
I stroked
my threadlike ghost

Annie Pia

The Man Who Was My Father

The dark man whose voice I can't recall
who was my father
offered me a boiled egg
one Sunday morning when it wasn't sunny
and you had left for Mass
when the gas hob in our ration book scullery was still
the pots, our story books of roots and rooting
of Italy and immigration, not needed,
they held their breath
and the bread bin where you kept the few pounds
my father couldn't find, kept your secret.
I can't recall if it was the yolk or the white
that I couldn't eat or why
but I can recall a room the colour of fudge
but without its sweetness
a tenement window which kept out the light
stale grass of our shared green below
the daily drudge of a pulley
my oversized cot a barren place.
And for the first time that morning I tasted frozen
like the chill on your face at some later time
at the opening of a door somewhere behind me
the draught of air that blew fear into your eyes
uncertain into mine as you did up my buttons
put me to bed, kissed me goodnight
and I didn't feel safe
and I saw him behind you waiting
for you to turn round
for the fairy tale to finish.
I can still see him now after your tears, the police and people
standing on the pavement below in standard gaberdine,
dance hall lights behind
the man who was my father.

Ann MacLaren

Early One Morning

When Lizzie's father collapsed at the table clutching his chest early one frosty winter morning, barely managing to gasp out a plea for help before vomiting his breakfast back onto his plate, Lizzie, only eight years old, knew exactly what to do. She dialled 999, explained the emergency, gave her full name and address together with instructions on how to get to their isolated cottage and, while waiting for help to arrive, mopped her father's brow with a cold cloth. She even, her grandmother would boast later, went with him in the ambulance to the hospital, although really this was because the ambulance driver didn't want to leave her alone at home. Everyone was so proud of her. If her mother had been alive she would have been proud of her too.

"If you hadn't acted so quickly your Daddy might have died," Lizzie's grandmother told her when she came to the hospital that afternoon to pick her up. She had cried then, big wet sobs as she buried her face in Granny's soft coat, and she had been cuddled and comforted.

"It's okay to cry, darling. You've been so brave today." And her grandmother, sure that Lizzie was thinking of her Mummy who had never come home from hospital, added: "Daddy will be back home with you again very soon."

Which had made her cry even more. Lizzie wondered if she should tell Granny that she didn't want to have Daddy back home. That she didn't like Daddy sometimes. That he scared her. She wanted to explain why, but didn't know what words to use. And Granny was a grown-up, like Daddy. Would she say Lizzie was being silly or nasty or spiteful? Just because Daddy came into bed at night with her sometimes. Just for a hug. A squeeze. A kiss. That's what Daddies do with their little girls, Granny would say. Touch and kiss. Your Daddy loves you, that's why he does that.

Lizzie's father had stayed in hospital for nearly three weeks. Three weeks of blissful happiness for Lizzie who couldn't bear to think about what would happen when her grandmother went away.

"Please take me home with you, Granny. I'd be such a good help to you, I promise. You must be so lonely living all alone. I could keep you company."

But Granny had told her how much she would hate living in the city when she was used to the countryside, and how she would miss all her school friends, and how lonely her Daddy would be without her. And then Daddy came back from the hospital, and soon after that Granny went home.

When Lizzie's father had his second heart attack, she acted just as swiftly as she had done four years before. It was early in the morning again, but this time he had finished his breakfast and was in the small toilet by the back door. He just managed to call out her name before collapsing onto the floor, where he lay, groaning, trousers round his ankles, wedged between the door and the toilet bowl.

Lizzie couldn't open the door, so she took a kitchen chair outside and climbed up onto it to look in through the small, open window. Her father's face, pressed against the cold floor, looked ghostly white, and he was sweating profusely. There was no noise coming from his slack mouth now, but she knew he was still alive because his eyes were opening and closing, as if that was the only painless movement he was able to make. Then they fixed on her at the window, staring.

Staring at her standing there in her thin, nylon nightie. The nightie that had been her mother's. He had told her to wear it because she looked so like her mother. Her warm, beautiful mother. Lizzie clutched her arms across her chest and shivered.

She jumped down from the chair and ran back into the house. She knew about the pills he kept in his jacket pocket, and how important it was to get one into his mouth quickly. So she knew exactly what to do.

Her father's jacket was hanging over a chair in the hall, and she quickly found the bottle of pills. There were only six left.

Lizzie tipped the six pills into her hand and put the empty bottle back into the jacket pocket. She went into the kitchen, poked the pills down through the sink drain, and turned on the cold tap to flush them away. Then she got washed and dressed for school. It was almost eight o'clock. She didn't feel like eating breakfast, but she poured herself a glass of milk and put a couple of biscuits into her schoolbag, in case she got hungry later. There was no sound from the toilet as she tiptoed past and slipped out of the back door to bring in the kitchen chair.

It was a long walk to the main road to catch the school bus, but Lizzie didn't mind. She had done it before, often, because her father worked on a farm, and sometimes, especially on early spring mornings like this, he would be off at the lambing. He didn't always drive her to the bottom of the lane. So nobody would be surprised when she told them, later, that she hadn't seen her father that morning, that he hadn't woken her before he left, but anyway, she always set her own alarm clock so she wouldn't be late for school. Somebody from the farm would ring up to find out why her father hadn't turned up for work, but there would be nobody to answer the phone. They would be annoyed, but she didn't think they would come looking for him. He was always taking time off without telling them beforehand. That was why he had to change his job so often.

It would be a big shock for Lizzie, finding her father dead when she got home from school, but she would be very brave. She would keep calm, just as she had done before. She would dial 999 and give her name and address, and instructions on how to get to the cottage. She would phone her grandmother, who would be very proud of her.

The bus would be along very soon. Lizzie looked around her at the familiar patchwork of fields with their crops and cows and sheep, at the fences and gates and gorse hedges, and at the crows flying overhead. She wondered what it would be like living in the city.

Beth Smith

A Builder's Tale From Inverness

I've worked in the building trade, all of my life,
married a loving bonnie wife,
had three fine sons, all grown now,
all of our kids, fair of brow.
Thought I'd be retired at seventy
but Tory policies mean I'm having tae
work building conservatories, for rich folk
with my old mates, who like to joke.
Auld Harry, he is eighty-two,
said, 'Ask the boy tae fetch a brew.'
I glanced around tae find a lad.
My old friends grinned, 'You've been had —
you're the boy aged seventy-one.'
Drank my tea in the Black Isle sun.

Helen Addy

Poundland Policeman

A life-sized policeman is stickered
to the automatic door of Poundland,
his Mona Lisa eyes keeping watch.
At the confectionery,
your daughter asks why he's there,
so you explain the power of suggestion,
how fear is peeled from the flimsiest backing.
She asks why his shoes don't touch the floor,
why his skin is always white,
so you explain how the law elevates him,
how white is the colour of respect.
At the till, she examines her brown hands,
the skin other kids won't touch.
Arms full of paid items, the door opens,
policeman shuddering as you both glide past.

Helen Addy

Escapology

Rising like a magician's coin,
the sun shimmers trees into nothing.
The solicitor's office
shuts out birdsong and light,
the glasses balanced
on his head the only windows,
the scratched lenses
slicing everything in half,
their smeared fingerprints
vanishing inside a handkerchief,
papers scattering like doves.

Sunday Fun

Mum insisted on a stroll round the block on her weekly visits. "It lets the air circulate through the cobwebs in my bonce." She laughed, still finding it funny after years of repetition.

"Yes mum," I agreed.

It got her away from the television, but I never saw what mum found from walking round a block of characterless semi-detached houses with badly painted fences and utilitarian gardens filled with kids' trampolines and sandpits. Sometimes, on good days, she made it to the park to feed the ducks. On this pleasant autumn afternoon, the park would be bursting with the fusty smell of fallen chestnuts and leaves piled high, ready to be jumped upon when no-one was watching. The avenues would be an artist's palette of russets and vermilions, ambers and golds. Burnt umber. The name stuck in my memory from somewhere. It reminded me of toffee apples and bonfires. An autumn colour. There might even be some squirrels. That might tempt mum. She loved watching their frisky games: "Like the bairns' high jinks." At three o'clock the sun was still doing its rounds, but it would be a bit nippy without gloves and a scarf, and in cold weather I knew the only walk for mum's arthritic knees and ankles would be round the square with a stop to pat the ginger cat at number twenty-one. That would mean passing the church hall.

"Do you think you'll manage the shops today?" I asked.

"Oh no, just round the square. Dr. Bryant warned me against too much exercise."

"What about the park? I've got some ends of bread for the ducks."

"The leaves will be far too slippy." Mum gave a shiver.

"Round the block it is then."

Maybe mum wouldn't notice the church hall. She could still see close up to knit intricate Aran patterns for the jumpers she made for Billy's kids, but her far sight was going. If I walked on the inside, she wouldn't see the hall until we'd passed it. Nobody could miss the church itself, a late Victorian victory of ostentation over taste: expensive grey stone imported from heaven knew where, with flying buttresses, gables and naturally a steeple with mischievous gargoyles trapped among the masonry — an architectural nightmare that only the town council could love. In contrast the hall was a modest seventies prefab squeezed between the Ionic arches of the church's grandiose entrance and the graveyard. To encourage people to keep their faith, or perhaps to remind them the building hadn't yet been transformed into a themed nightclub, the church committee had erected a notice-board outside the hall. Eye-catching colours proclaimed messages such as *CH..CH — What's missing? UR*, or *Jesus is for life, not just for Christmas*. The clichés got changed whenever some bright spark had another eureka moment. With the schools back and Halloween not far away, the church remembered the young people in the town and had decided to devote October to them. The neon poster on the notice-board blazoned out *Sunday is Fun Day*.

Forty years on to the day, that was what I didn't want mum to see. Sunday is fun day. Silly really, because dad loved slogans.

Dad worked Monday to Friday nine till six, and Saturdays until one, as a works clerk. Saturday afternoons found him following his own religion at the town's football ground, and in the evenings he discussed the finer points of the match with his mates in the pub. He supported the team from the day he was lifted onto his grandad's shoulders to watch them lift the region cup (for the first and only time) until they cremated the old man in his blue and yellow scarf to the doleful resonance of the team's anthem. That was dad's week, but Sundays he kept free for his family — mum, Billy and me.

"Catriona," — he would bounce me up and down even when I was up to mum's chest — "what day is it?"

"Sunday," I would say.

"Billy, what does that mean?"

"Sunday is fun day," Billy would yell. "Yeah."

Sunday is fun day.

On Sundays we got to pick where we'd go for a family day out, although in those days the choices were limited to the park, the seaside, the cinema, the museum or the zoo. We never chose the museum. Dad didn't drive. The selection depended on public transport, the weather and how close it was to the end of the month — dad's pay day. On the day I remember, forty years ago, Billy wanted to go to the zoo. An outsider romped home in the big race with dad's fiver riding on its nose, so we got to pick big.

"They've got a Siberian tiger." Billy stuck the local newspaper under our noses to prove it. "He's called Ivan. Ivan the Terrible."

"It's my turn to choose," I stomped. "I want to go on a boat trip."

"A boat trip?" My parents gaped. Where had this come from? The local park had a few pre-war rowing boats, but it wasn't safe to keep them in the water after the end of August. Anyway a couple of strokes took you from one side of the pond to the other. Nobody could call that a boat trip.

"The *Titanic* was a hundred-and-four feet high from keel to bridge and weighed forty-six-thousand-three-hundred-and-twenty-eight tons," I recited from Mrs. Blackthorn's book. "It was built in Belfast, had nine decks and could go at a maximum speed of twenty-four knots." We were studying the heyday of liners in history. Boats were 'in' at school.

"It sank, didn't it?" Dad said. He didn't get the point. Liners were luxury. Liners were glamorous. Liners were a million nautical miles away from the routine greyness of a seventies suburban childhood.

"What about the loch?" Mum said, frowning at me. "They must do pleasure trips."

Getting to the loch meant two buses, a train and a mile long walk, but I was sticking to my guns. Billy groaned.

"It takes ages to get there. We'll no sooner have arrived than we'll have to turn back."

I stuck out my tongue.

"It gets dark by six these days," Mum added.

Dad was about to agree with the others, so I wiped out the snarl and replaced it with a near-to-tears pout. I knew dad wouldn't refuse his little doll.

"Right, we'd better get started then. We can go to the zoo another Sunday, Billy. The tiger will be there for a while." He raised his hands and curled his fingers like tiger claws and pretended to growl. Billy tossed the paper on the floor. Mum picked it up and edged towards the kitchen.

"Don't bother making any sandwiches, mum. I'll treat us to lunch in a café." Dad rattled the coins in his pocket to show off his riches. Mum pursed her lips. I was the only one smiling.

Billy gave me the cold shoulder on the journey. Dad went out of the railway carriage to roll his tobacco and mum read a knitting magazine. It was too late to change my mind although if I was honest, I'd rather have seen the tiger. I squashed my nose against the mud-stained window and watched the rows of houses change to rows of barren fields. The train pulled into the station and dad hustled us out, while mum checked the times of the trains home. The boat trips left on the hour and by the time we trudged from the railway station to the pier we just missed one. The passengers were taking photographs of landlubber friends on the shore as the waves splashed their best shoes. Dad checked his watch as we headed towards the park. I guessed he was wondering if there was time to nip to the pub before the boat returned. A glare from mum put him in his place.

"There's an ice-cream van. Can we have a cone, dad?" Billy's whine reminded dad that he was there under sufferance.

Dad looked at his coins and did a head count. The train fare was more than he bargained for.

"Ice-cream? In October? Are you mad?"

"Not for me, love." Mum was tactful.

"I want a flake and strawberry sauce on mine," I said.

"Greedy." Billy nudged me and I gave him a shove.

"Stay here and behave," Dad warned.

We watched him cross to the van. A group of teenage boys were kicking a football on the other side of the road. They stopped their game to let dad pass, until one of them spotted dad's scarf.

"What's with the scarf, mate?"

Dad was wearing his football scarf. He always did. Billy pointed. The boys, to a man, were sporting the colours of the team's main rivals. I suppose, like us, they were here on a day trip from town. Dad ignored the barrage of taunts that followed, ducking as their ball was shot towards him. He just about made it safely back with the ice-cream. Strawberry sauce dribbled down his wrist, but he forgot my flake.

"Hooligans. Let's move on." He jerked his head towards the swing park as he handed us the cones.

"Running away, just like your team," the leader of the gang jeered.

One of the boys threw a stone. It was never intended to hit us, but mum was getting nervy. I could see her looking round for a friendly bobby. We pretended to enjoy ourselves, but the roundabout was stiff and the slide was sticky and covered in wet leaves. The gang didn't tire of their fun. They moved to the play area after us and slouched against the gate drinking from bottles of lager that they passed between them. Dad was fuming, but he wouldn't start anything in front of us. He checked his watch every five minutes while mum tried to calm him.

"Time to get back for the boat," he decided.

The boys moved to let us through, but the leader stretched out his leg to trip dad up. "Diver." The others laughed as dad stumbled.

91

I could smell lager on their breaths. One of them looked only a few years older than me. He was certainly no taller. He had a cute face. When he saw me staring at him he looked away.

Dad made sure we kept a good pace back to the pier. We didn't look behind us, but we knew the boys were following us. At the ticket booth they were still behind us.

"Five pounds for a family ticket round the loch." Dad read the notice aloud. A droplet of rain fell on the advertisement board, smudging the ink. Mum looked at the gathering grey clouds and put her hand out to test the weather.

"Maybe we shouldn't bother going round. I spotted a nice café across the road. We could go there instead."

Billy looked pleased, but dad was set. We came for a boat trip and a boat trip we would have, even if it killed him. I wasn't brave enough to admit defeat, so I took hold of dad's hand and marched towards the ticket seller.

"A family ticket round the loch, please," I said to the lady behind the desk.

Dad handed over his last five pound note and took the ticket. We waited in the make-shift shelter for the boat to arrive. Billy kicked the back of his seat while I counted the fat ducks on the shore waiting for passers-by to toss them scraps from their picnics. It made me hungry. The rain seemed to have deterred the gang, and mum became chattier once the boys wandered off.

"There's a bit of sun now."

It was still a chilly autumn afternoon. Too chilly for an open-topped steamer.

"I'm frozen," Billy complained.

"Should have worn your jumper," I answered.

"Stop arguing," said dad.

When the *Loch Princess* arrived it looked nothing like the *Titanic*. There was no gorgeous dance floor with staircases and candelabras. There was no orchestra and no first class lounge with a grand piano. There were no officers in gold braid uniforms and ladies in silk frocks and glitzy heels. It was a rusty yellow bathtub that smelled of diesel. There was no-one on the shore to wave to as we trundled aboard.

"We'll sit here." Dad picked a bench under a torn canopy. He was still ducking round to make sure none of the football lads got on, or if they did, to report them to the skipper.

The captain blew the ship's horn and we set off, churning up the loch and scaring the ducks. The rain hadn't come to anything, but the boat's wooden deck was a bit slippy.

"Watch you don't fall," Mum warned as I got up to explore.

"Are you coming Billy?"

"There's nothing to see."

I went on my own. Billy was right, there wasn't much to see. The boat had an indoor seating area they called a 'lounge' and a 'restaurant' that sold bacon rolls, tea and chips. I scrambled back outside as the boat rounded the small island in the centre of the loch. There were supposed to be deer on the island, or so the advertising poster claimed. I looked over the side, holding tightly to the safety bar. The metal rattled. A woman on my right pointed something out to her young son. I looked where she pointed, but I could only see trees, no deer. Instead, I noticed the cute looking boy a few feet away to my left, hanging over the rails. At first I thought it was bravado, but then I realised he was being sick. Not so brave now. He saw me and gave a pale smile. I smiled back. I looked around, but couldn't see dad. It was safe to sidle down the boat to talk to the boy.

"You were in the park," I said.

"Yeah." He blushed.

His name was Jimmy. He told me he hadn't drunk lager before, and the movement of the boat combined with the tarry aroma and the smell of chips coming from the canteen wasn't helping his stomach. He was twelve and came from our town, not far from where we lived. He went to the high school I would be going to the following year. His parents went to the bingo every Sunday and he was forced to spend the day dragging along after his elder brother. The 'spotty one', he called him. Jimmy didn't like his brother's friends. He wanted to go to the zoo.

"They've got a new tiger. From Russia."

"Yeah, I know."

Jimmy made the tiger sound like a cold war spy.

"I'm Catriona," I said. "You can call me Cat."

I held out my hand the way I saw adults introduce themselves, but before Jimmy could shake it, dad was upon us. He was raging at Jimmy, his face purple.

"You keep your hands off my girl."

"Dad, don't," I cried, defending my new friend.

"Let go of me."

Fists were raised and within seconds the rest of the gang were on the deck beside us.

"What's going on?"

"Leave off my kid brother, you bast…"

Someone shoved me and I stepped back, holding my hands over my ears. I was caught in a blur of elbows, angry faces, alcoholic breath and swearing. There was a scuffle, the ripping of wood, a fall and a crack like a giant boiled egg opening. I screamed. Mum was beside me, hands over her mouth in shock.

"What is it, mum?" I heard Billy's voice, but I didn't see him.

For a second the whole boat shook. Then the ship's bell rang. The engine stopped and the captain was asking questions. The crew were shouting instructions at one another and life jackets were thrown overboard as the passengers pointed. Bubbles formed on the water then disappeared. Everyone was talking, but I couldn't hear a thing.

"Dad?" I looked around. "Dad, where are you?"

That was forty years ago to the day. In the carfuffle, the boat's railing had given way. Lunging forwards, dad slipped on the wet deck and hit his head before falling into the thrashing waters of the loch. He never surfaced.

There were only a few people at the inquest: representatives from the boat company and the father of one of the boys. The court heard that the boat was old and that the railings should have been checked before the 'Loch Princess' left the pier. The company was ordered to pay a fine, but no individual was held accountable. The general opinion was that my father had brought it on himself. The boys were acting in self-defence. Witnesses on the boat saw dad threaten Jimmy. There was talk of him being drunk, but that was untrue. My caring father, unable to defend himself, was branded an alcoholic thug, and it was my fault.

Billy never forgave me. I wasn't invited to his wedding. I'd never met his children, my niece and nephew. Forty years of memories and misery later, it was still my fault.

Sunday is fun day.

I helped mum on with her coat.

"Thanks, love. It's no fun growing old on your own."

I held back a tear. We hadn't spoken of dad during dinner, but he was never far from mum's thoughts. There had never been anyone else for her. I closed the garden gate and we made our way silently down the road towards the church. As we reached the corner a drop of rain bounced off the pavement.

"I knew I should have brought my brolly," said mum.

I looked upwards. There was hardly a cloud dotting the sky. "The forecast said it would be dry. Maybe it will go off."

"Maybe," mum agreed, "but let's not bother going round. I spotted a nice café across the road. Let's go there instead."

Rona Fitzgerald

Dark Matter

Swaddled in obsidian layers, hunched, hidden,
wearing his world on his back. He never asks
for anything but searches the bins for waste.

Sleeping in the air — under soft green bushes in summer
doorways in denuded winter — he spends the day walking
reciting Shakespeare, a fool or a king by turns.

I once spoke to a woman who slept in the hallway
of the National Library in Dublin. She said the black
helped her to disappear, to care less and to be free.

Rona Fitzgerald

Mullingar

When it was my turn to go with dad to Mullingar
for the Christmas bird, I was always excited
and nervous with thoughts about the journey
from Raheny through winter ravaged towns.
Memories of stopping to piddle at spiky hedgerows,
dad's impatience, and in the end, the turkey dangling
on a hook, dead and mottled like a discarded toy.

Certainty

I wake still holding the edge
of your sleeve, it is winter
but the light tries to fool me.
It is snowing, I am drifting

between worlds, the thread
of years like spider veins
inks my skin, a crisscross
of seasons on my tongue.

I close my eyes
I refuse to let go.

Eileen Carney Hulme

From The Great Book Of Distances

Donald tells me he is afraid
of leaving and having left
wakes in the night, thinking
of trees and roads and ghosts.
He wants to telephone, to know
we are OK but trees have no
numbers, roads are endless
and the ghosts do not reply.
So he gets up puts the kettle on
remembers Dan and his music —
wonders why the distance between
here and there is never less.

Ian Donough

Sugar Town

He found himself in Sugar Town
skulking through
an atmosphere so sweet
his teeth ached.

And his heart felt moist as cake...

Sugar Town citizens
with liquorice eyes,
puddings for heads,
shimmied the candy street.

He asked himself
'How did I get to Sugar Town?'

Knees like coconuts,
muscles wrapped in fudge,
struggling against a sherbet breeze,
scraping paving stones with toffee feet,
knowing underneath was solid meat.

Ian Donough

Tarragona

If there was nothing more to think about;
if our minds had been rubbed
bluer than the faded blue
of this thin sky that hardly seems
to cover decently
the monstrous universe above;
if this statue of Richard De Lucia
climbed down and slept among the pigeons,
triumphs and mortifications
lost among their soothing coo and babble;
if the railway that runs by the beach
rusted, quiet within its iron heat;
if traffic spluttered out like a spent candle,
still I would sing to you, my eyes
full of you, your imprint everywhere.

Learning To Smile

I've been learning how to smile. It's not as easy as it sounds. Not when I'm not sure when to smile in the first place, but I'm trying to learn. I'm good at learning things. Dave — he's my Educational Psychologist — says I'm getting better at it but that I should try not to take it so seriously. My mum just laughs and says I look like I'm in pain. Me, I think I look like one of the Picasso paintings we were studying in Art last period. Features twisted and in all the wrong places. Smiling is difficult when you don't feel it inside you but Dave says it will help me fit in better so I'll give it a try.

Dave shows me all these pictures of people and it says underneath how those people are feeling. I'm supposed to try and remember them. Sometimes facial expressions can help make sense of what people are saying, Dave says. It's supposed to help me understand what people mean when they talk — especially when they don't say what they mean. Why would someone say what they didn't mean? Why not just say what you mean in the first place? And it doesn't always. Help, I mean. Sometimes it makes it even more complicated.

The other day I thought I would give smiling a try. The girl I sit beside in Maths was talking to another girl at our table about a boy and she smiled when she finished talking, so I smiled too. After class the other girl shoved me against the wall and threatened me. Apparently, they thought I was laughing at her because her boyfriend dumped her. Dave says that maybe it was a sad smile to cover up how hurt she was. Dave doesn't have a photo of that expression on his cards or on my worksheet. I checked. Still, at least they knew I was trying to smile.

I still don't get it quite right every time. That's why I'm staring at my reflection in the glass of the bus window trying to get my face to match up with the pictures on the worksheet. It's the end of the actual school day but just the start of the worst bit. Sixteen miles of country roads home, stuck on a bus with a bunch of neds who just happen to live nearby. Taunted about everything; who my friends are, who my friends aren't, not got any friends. It doesn't matter what I say or do, it's the wrong thing. Sometimes they've heard rumours about the things I've done that day, or a different day, or at a different school (seven so far), or when I was wee. Sometimes it's just name-calling. Sometimes they just make it up. It never makes much sense.

It confuses me why they bother to spend so much of their time on me when they say they don't like me. I don't think about them that much. Just on the bus really. One of them leans over from the seat in front, his face going through an intricate series of expressions framed by the fuzzy bus seats. I try to understand them at the start but they change too fast and I just don't care enough to bother. I'm pretty sure none of them is a smile, though. I'm concentrating so hard on his face that I don't hear most of what he says. Then he leans further over, squashed in the gap between the seats, and looks at my worksheet.

"What's the window-licker up to now?" he asks. He's an ugly boy, face riddled with freckles. I'm glad I don't look like him. An older boy on the bus has the same freckles but they have different surnames. My mum says this Freckles's mother is a bit of a slapper. Tried to steal her best friend's man. If he was as freckly as his kids I can't see why he's so popular. I ignore Freckles and go back to staring out the window, although I do wonder about practising my angry face.

"How can you just ignore that?" asks Vikki who sits beside me most days. She also goes to Learning Support and sometimes comes in for the sort of comments I get.

"Hmm," I say vaguely. The anti-bullying advice we get at school says not to let them see that it's bothering me, to try to ignore it and not react. My mum said I have that one down pat, but then she laughed and told me that if all of what the leaflet said was true I'd never be bullied again. I wish it was true.

For about ten minutes I think Freckles has given up and continue my facial contortions in the glass. Happy, sad, confused, angry, happy, sad... Then a half-eaten sandwich gets tossed in my lap followed by a not-quite-empty can of Coke. As they don't belong to me I just drop them back over the seat.

Freckles complains loudly about the Coke dripping down his face. He stands up and steps towards me but the bus driver shouts. Freckles looks at me with a very unpleasant expression on his face — so unpleasant that even I can recognise it as such although I'm not sure exactly what it means. He'll leave me alone for a while now, though. At least until he thinks the driver has stopped looking in the mirror.

Freckles is part of a large group who always sit together on the bus. They're talking now about meeting up that night at the bus stop outside the shop. Now normally, I like bus stops. They're useful when I want to get out the village for a while but I can't see the attraction for more than a few minutes. And who wants to stand outside the shop? Outside? I mean I like the shop. I like to go in and buy sweets sometimes, even some odd messages for my mum if she thinks I can manage. This lot just hang around at the bus stop and let the hourly buses go past them without getting on. Sometimes they call the people getting off names. They hardly ever go into the shop either although sometimes they ask someone else to go and get them something or dare each other to go in. They talk about the five-finger discount they get. I don't get a discount in there. It's quite an expensive shop. Most nights they smoke cigarettes which make them cough and smell bad, and swig Buckie as if it tasted nice.

I'm never invited to join them. I wouldn't want to, anyway. Why would I want to stand outside in the rain and the cold, smoking and drinking and making myself feel sick? I'd rather sit at home with mum and do something, even if it's just watch the telly. In the warmth and comfort of the living room. Even if it means spending time with my little brother. He's much nicer than the people at the bus stop. They stand too close to each other, as well. I don't like people getting too close to me and I hate being touched. I let my mum give me quick hugs sometimes now, but when I was younger it made me start to scream. Sometimes that made her cry and I didn't like that, but I liked my space more.

I heard one of my teachers talking to another teacher one day in the corridor. She was saying that she didn't think there was anything wrong with me. She thought I was a nice girl and so well-behaved, perfectly normal. I am a nice girl. I am well-behaved. But sometimes, just sometimes, I'm not perfect, or normal. Sometimes, when there is too much going on around me I want to scream. Other people don't like it when I scream. They don't like it when I shout, either, or lash out with my hands or my feet. Nor do they like it when I bang my head against the wall repeatedly even though that doesn't affect anyone else.

There aren't many girls who are like me. I've only met one, at my last school, and she was really weird. My teacher said that she thinks Dave is making it up because he's writing a book about autism and wants at least one girl to include. They kept talking about labelling pupils. All I know is that most of the things Dave tells me to try seem to help, so I think he does know what he's talking about. He doesn't need to label us either. Only about ten people go to see him regularly and he knows all our names.

Anyway, my teacher doesn't think I'm so normal now. It wasn't intentional, but the very next week after I heard her talking I threw my chair across her classroom. It wasn't really my fault though. A boy was pinging rubbers at my head. He had spent the first ten minutes of the class sawing up rubbers with a plastic knife from the cafeteria and then started pinging them at my head. One after the other after the other. It was going to go on for the rest of the lesson. It often does. Most of the time I just wait until the end of the class and then check my hair. One time a teacher shouted at me for making a mess on the floor with all the bits so I started screaming. That was my last day at that school. I'm getting better, though. At coping. At ignoring. He'd pinged quite a lot of rubbers before I threw the chair. A few years ago it would only have taken one bit of rubber and I probably wouldn't have stopped at just one chair.

After that, however, all of the staff agreed that I wasn't quite right. The discussions started again about whether this was the right environment for me and so on. Dave talked about how much progress I'd made at the Review Meeting and as no-one could think of anywhere else to send me I got to stay here. The Head Teacher asked me if I was happy about that and I said I was. She said I didn't look happy about it. Dave just sighed, put his hand on his forehead and shook his head but I got to stay.

The bus reaches my stop and as I go to get off I have to pass Freckles. His foot is out to trip me up so I pretend to. My elbow makes contact with his face. Hard. He sits there shrieking like a girl. The bus driver looks at me as I walk down the aisle. He gets up and speaks to him. As I step off the bus I turn and see scarlet smeared across the freckles.

"Oi! Wait up!" shouts the driver so I step onto the pavement and wait. The driver steps off and closes the door behind him. I wait for the yelling and the accusations and the threats to start but they don't. I turn to look at the driver, staring at a spot just beside his right ear. I have found that it is the furthest away from someone's eyes that I can look, without getting shouted at and made to meet their eyes.

"Nice shot," the driver says and I think he might be smiling. "He's a right wee shite. Now, if anyone asks I gave you a row, okay?" I nod and he gets back onto the bus and drives off.

I make my way home. When I step into the kitchen, all my practice on the bus seems to have paid off as my mum looks at me in surprise and says, "What are you smiling about?"

First prize winner of the inaugural Federation of Writers (Scotland) story competition in 2013.

Gerry McCulloch

Me

See me?
See pubs?
Ah luv pubs!
Ah couldnae drink a whole wan, bu'.

See me?
See sheep?
Ah luv sheep!
Ah couldnae eat a whole wan, bu'.

See me?
See weans?
Ah luv weans!
Ah couldnae skelp a whole wan, bu'.

See me?
See crosswords?
Ah luv crosswords!
Ah couldnae dae a whole wan, bu'.

See me?
See opera?
Ah luv opera!
Ah couldnae stawn a whole wan, bu'.

See me?
See mountains?
Ah luv mountains!
Ah couldnae climb a whole wan, bu'.

See me?
See balloons?
Ah luv balloons!
Ah couldnae blow-up a whole wan, bu'.

Gerry McCulloch

See me?
See promises?
Ah luv promises!
Ah couldnae keep a whole wan, bu'.

See me?
See fish?
Ah hate fish.

Sixty Seven Minutes

we are the little people
scuffling through life
head down, collar up
standing at the shipyard gate
praying for a nod
empty bellies wait at home
staring at the clock
dreading footsteps in the close
a mother's shoulders tensed
sixty seven minutes
the pause between work and hunger
sixty seven minutes for life to change
footsteps on the quay
a ten hour shift on a heel of bread
an envelope of hope at the end of the day
footsteps in the close
bairns raise their heads
little fledglings chirping their hope
eased into the chair by the fire
wet boots pulled and stuffed with paper
hands grip a cup of steaming tea
a wife's loving kiss
another day survived

Ian Noble

In Liguria

Did you notice
the lemon picker's bucket
that rests on the terrace
beside the peach nets
while he dozes in the shade
of the street that is no wider
than a handshake...

Or the old lady in her pale blue dress,
running her fingers through her short
grey hair with the memory of a curl,
bleached by sun and age,
as she climbs the steps towards
the ratchet press, where juices
still flow from the rind...

And did you find yourself
back home, walking a little more
slowly — savouring the bitter
rain as it bounces across your window
pane, reflecting northern light —
smiling at the memory of a ruin
lizard as it scampers towards the shade?

Ian Noble

Lutalo's Beat

He would love to learn —
to make bricks with the men in the village
as they tap-a-tap-tap to release
the mud from the mould. If he made
a good one, he would sleep with it in his bed.

But for now, he must wait
at home, turning and twisting cassava
and sweet potato in his hand and across his nose,
exploring their landscapes
with his fingertips.

He works so hard in the garden
where the family food is grown.
Taking care of the maize — tilling
and turning and cutting everything —
even if it isn't ready. He tills and cuts
though the seedlings can't take it.
And his family scold him — even though
he has worked so hard.

So, he runs to the banana plantation. Running
like he did when the villagers came, waving
their *pangas* because he screamed at night
and they thought he was bewitched. Running,
as his toes feel the twists and turns, towards
his special tree, where he hides his sticks —
where he sits with his back to the bark,
tap, tap, tapping them against his ear.

Back home, in the evening, he rests
on his grandfather's weary chest —
breathing in the age, with his sticks
tapping gently at his ear.
"I am too old to chase you now, Lutalo,"

as the elder reaches for his *namunjoloba* —
fingertips ready to converse through the drum-skin
as his 'tips' respond the 'taps.'

Tap-tap-tap... Tip-tip-tip
Tappa-tap-tap... Tippa-tip-tip
Tappa-tappa-tappa-tap... Tippa-tippa-tippa-tip
Tap... Tippa-tip
Tappa-tap... Tip
Tap

Together.

Birthday Present

When I was seven or eight years old,
I was given a shilling for my birthday.
A beautiful coin;
just the right size to be what it was
and to mean what it meant,
but I dropped it.

Lost in the grass
and gone without trace.

Had I been asked,
'What did you use it for?
What did you spend it on?'
I could have said,

'I used it to buy time,' or,
'I bought time with it.'
A single square of time,
with sunshine, grass and clover stalks;
buttercups in bloom and silver falling.

But I did not know that then.

North Third

'Do you think that with such maps
a man might discover his place?'

'Yes, because I have already discovered North Third
with the soft wind caressing the beech slope
where broom grows
and the turf thumps
and in the west
an indescribable space
that made us conscious of air.'

'I remember that now,
how this chart shows
what can only be called
a nice day.
Were we to open another one,
might it be raining?'

'Probably not, because once the sun shines on places like these
it produces a lightness
almost impossible to erase.
Besides, this is an area prone to nostalgia
like Malaga,
Benidorm
or the pier at Weston-Super-Mare.'

Moonrise

The Polish Soul
rises above the Tatras mountains
and dissolves across the plains of the Vistula.
It glides slowly over frozen ground
and weeps as the leaves fall.

It is a fire that warms
but does not burn.
It has eyes that look
but do not see.
Pain is its home,
sorrow its tongue
and muted its call.
But it hangs like a star in the east
over a child
in its rich stall.

Love And The Sea

It is night, and the sky is full of stars. Peat smoke drifts on the breeze. I stand at the edge of the sea, and step into the cold water, feeling it revive me. I walk forward, my senses sharpen, and I am unburdened. I am free again. I ease my body into the water, and let it carry my weight. My land bound clumsiness is gone, and I am graceful once more. I am a part of the ocean. I am part of all life there. I shrug off my loneliness as easily as I have cast off my clothes on the empty beach.

There is a risk, of course, there is always a risk. But my nearest neighbours are two miles off, and there is little cause for anyone to be walking at night, here on this secluded beach. Tonight, Mark is away on a business trip, leaving me here, with only the birds and the seals for company. I feel a pang of guilt. Should I be missing him? Is it right that I prefer the gentle embrace of the ocean?

Sometimes my life with him seems to be only a strange dream. The sea is my only reality, my only home. I lean back in the water, letting my hair drift like a tangle of seaweed. I look up at the sky, and I am floating in an ocean of stars, basking in moonlight. I close my eyes. Water laps at my skin.

The next day, Mark is due back. My guilt has made me try harder, spending the day shopping and cooking and cleaning. I only stop for a little while at lunchtime, to stare out of the window, at the vast expanse of ocean. The wind has got up, and the clouds are scurrying across the sky. I feel mesmerised by it, by the changing colours of sea and sky. I feel the tug of the ocean, as if we are still connected.

By the time he arrives, everything is in its place, just as he likes it. I kiss him on the cheek, inhale the scent of sweat and aftershave as I hug him. He looks crumpled, the top buttons of his shirt undone, one of them hanging by a thread. It bothers me, this loose button, and I want to pull it off, but something stops me from committing this act of easy familiarity. I listen as he tells me about his trip, about the delays to his flight, the lack of taxis.

He is away a lot these days. I often wonder if I am enough for him. I am pulled by the deep, and he is a being of air, of flight.

I keep our conversations light and banal. I don't tell him about my moonlit swim. He doesn't like me going off by myself at night. He thinks the sea is dangerous. And it is. But not to me. How can I explain this?

He goes through to the bedroom to unpack, and I hear him thumping about the room. I feel suddenly achingly lonely. I feel afraid, and I don't know why.

I slip out of the front door, feel the breeze against my skin. The sun is sinking into the ocean, the colours glowing orange and gold against a turquoise sky. I try to release the tightness in my belly, to find my breath again, but it's as if someone has their hand against my throat, crushing me, making me gasp for air. I sink to the ground, and stay there, curled into myself, until my breathing becomes easier.

That night sleep eludes me. I wait until I hear Mark's breathing become slow and steady, then I slip out of bed, pulling on a cardigan over my thin nightgown. I feel strange, insubstantial. I go into the kitchen, and stand at the window, filling a glass from the tap. I almost feel unable to grip the weight of the glass. I am a ghost, trespassing on my own life. I am a shadow cast by the moon. I sip the cool water whilst I watch the moonlight break through the clouds, glinting on the sea. Dark, dangerous, beautiful. I put down the glass and go outside.

When I reach the sand, I slip off my clothes, drop them on the beach, walk into the shallows. I feel my skin change, thickening, reacting to the water. The tightness in my throat and belly has gone. I feel much calmer. I step forward, deeper, feeling the coarse sand against my feet, the cold water against my skin. When my feet can no longer touch the bottom, I kick into the sea, my eyes adjusting to the moonlight, my hands pulling me on. I notice the seals on the rocks lurch forward on their bellies, then slip into the sea. I feel different now, and I know I can no longer go back to the old world. I have left it behind. Here, in the black ocean, I find my peace. I kick my feet like a tail, disappear into the water, and finally, I find my way home.

Susie Stewart

How Useful To Be A Chameleon

How useful to be a chameleon,
changing colour according to mood.
Blood red for a terrible temper
and blue if I want to be rude.

I'll be black when I'm feeling downhearted
and green on the first day of spring.
Bright orange when yielding to passion
and pink if I just need a fling.

Strong brown as the leaves turn in autumn;
turquoise when eating gateaux.
Golden while swimming in Cyprus
and purple as age starts to show.

Yolk yellow's the colour in summer,
pure white when there's snow in the air.
I'll be tartan while riding a camel
with tangerine streaks in my hair.

How useful to be a chameleon,
changing colour according to mood.
But on balance I'd rather be human.
Chameleons eat spiders not food.

Going Home

My boots were scuffed brown leather, caked in mud, but sturdy and waterproof. These were boots I could have adventures in. Boots I could put on and escape the city. Boots I could use to become someone else for a while, someone wilder, freer, braver.

These were boots that could defy squelching peat bogs, traverse torrents of water with ease. Boots that could scale mountains, shrink vast ranges to manageable hills. They could push onwards through pain, blisters, and hour after hour of relentless rain that left my hair plastered to my face, dripping into my eyes, changing the landscape to a grey-soaked murk.

I got them when I was fourteen, when I became involved in my local Duke of Edinburgh's Award scheme. I also got a compass, a map holder, a massive blue backpack and a bright orange survival bag. This was all very exciting. I had not known that survival bags existed until then, but as soon as I got one, I secretly longed to use it on one of my expeditions. Because we weren't supposed to use them except in dire circumstances, it was a bit like wanting to press the emergency stop button on the escalator.

I soon became familiar with the world of camping stoves, dried food, and having to pee in bushes. I learnt how to use a map and a compass. I made friends as we tied wonky looking bandages onto each other. We plotted routes on our maps, trying to imagine how the landscape would look in real life, and learnt how to time our journeys. Those closely pressed contour lines did nothing to convey the splendour and the harshness of the mountains. I lived in the suburbs, where I was always close to shops, supermarkets, houses, telephone boxes. I was skinny and unused to carrying heavy loads on my back. I wondered how I would cope with it all.

After a few practice walks in the local hills, where we ambled along some well-maintained paths, it was soon time to head out to the wilds for the real thing. For our first expedition, we would be camping out on the Isle of Arran for several days, following a winding route over the mountains. Due to a curious turn of fate, we were heading for the very house which used to belong to my grandmother.

She had died the year before, and I missed her, in an aching, wordless sort of way. But I also missed the island to which I had come to belong. I had spent my summers in her little cottage, learning to bake, playing on the beaches. When it rained I lay on my bed and read the Broons annual and ate bars of Fry's chocolate cream.

So it was with a sense of returning home, that I boarded the ferry with this assorted group of teens. Some of them I knew, but others were strangers. I wondered how we would get along.

I stood on the deck and watched the familiar outline of hills grow closer. The Sleeping Warrior, they called it. When we arrived in Brodick harbour, I almost expected to find my grandmother standing there, waiting to take us back home in her ancient burgundy Rover. I remembered her little dog sitting in my lap, with its sharp claws digging into my legs as we rounded the bends. I would squeal and hug the dog closer to me. Now we were bundled into our organisers' cars, squashed up against each other. But the place, the road, everything was just the same.

When we arrived at the house, I longed to run in, to call out to my grandmother, to raid the biscuit tin in the kitchen for French Fancies or Battenberg cake. But the organisers wouldn't let me, saying it was part of the rules that we stayed outside. I suppose they thought it was character building. But I was happy just to be there. Happy just to be home. With a lot of giggling, we managed to put up our tent in a way which looked reasonably secure. Inside it was very snug, very orange. We got into our sleeping bags and went to sleep. I liked the sound of the rain on the tent, the smell of the grass.

The next day, I groggily ate breakfast, which consisted of a small packet of sugary cereal. I resisted the temptation to eat it by tipping the contents straight from the packet into my mouth, and poured it into a plastic bowl, sloshing milk over it. I still wanted to get into the house, but I couldn't think how. Perhaps I could sneak in later, when no one was looking. I was ever keen to avoid adult scrutiny. I liked being left to myself, not having to pretend I was doing something useful. I simply liked to wander, to explore, to cycle and to run about with the dog. At home idleness was frowned upon, but on Arran, nobody seemed to care.

With an effort, I brought myself back to the present. Everyone was getting ready to go, climbing into waterproofs, fastening their rucksacks and checking that they had everything. We were to begin our expedition into the mountains, but fog had descended. Should we go? The organisers thought the fog would probably lift soon enough, so off we went. I was in a group of five, all girls between fourteen and sixteen. Mobile phones had not been invented yet. We were to rely on ourselves. What could possibly go wrong?

All went well until we began to climb the mountain, moving further into the descending fog. One of the girls, Elaine, wasn't happy. The rest of us thought we should go on. After all, we had our maps and our compasses to guide us if we got lost. As we climbed higher, Elaine became more and more upset, and just when we had got to the top of the mountain, she refused to go any further. In spite of all our persuasions, she would not budge. It was cold and damp, and we were surrounded by fog, so to keep ourselves warm, we got into our survival bags. Finally, I thought, a chance to use them. Our training had not anticipated this situation, and we had no idea what to do next, other than wait for help.

Our rescuers did not materialise. The day was drawing on, and we realised we were in danger of becoming stuck on the mountain alone at night. Dragging Elaine behind us, ignoring her protests and her crying, we used our compasses to navigate through the thick fog. For the first time, I was afraid. The night was close on our heels.

Further and further we walked, our legs heavy and aching, our hearts pounding, but the fog remained all around us. We were tired, and cold, and hungry, and afraid. The light was almost gone now. Our boots squelched into soft mud. To stop ourselves being so afraid, we talked about what we would like for dinner when we got in. I fantasised about roast chicken and mashed potatoes with gravy. I thought about how warm and cosy the house would be. I felt it was waiting for me to return. I could not think about the mud and the dark and the silent mountain.

Eventually, I saw something below me which looked like a river, but it made no sound. I walked towards it, and as I neared it, I realised it was not a river, but a narrow road. We had reached civilisation. Oh, my joy at finding that road. Never had I seen such a beautiful road, never had the solid tarmac against my boots felt so good. We walked downhill towards the sea, and soon we came to a cottage. Inside I could see a young man busying himself about the kitchen. He was oblivious to the group of teens looking in his window. For a moment I felt transfixed by the strangeness of the situation, hesitant at knocking on his door, for there was surely no one else around for miles. One of the others plucked up the courage and knocked at his door. I could see his face, startled in the window. He opened the door, surely not expecting to see a group of young girls, alone on the hills at night. We explained what had happened and his concerned face turned to a smile. He offered us a lift back to my grandmother's cottage. He talked and talked as we drove back in his Landrover. The moon was glinting off the sea.

It turned out that the man was a forester. "I go up the hills just in my jeans and my trainers, and you go up with all your compasses and your maps and all your gear and you still manage to get into trouble. It's kind of funny," he said.

Hilarious, I thought, biting my tongue. I did not want to risk getting swiftly ejected from the car for some cheeky comment. The adrenaline which had been flowing through my body was beginning to abate, and I felt now I would never manage the short journey home on foot.

It was so good to return. The organisers felt so sorry us, for what we had been through, that we did not have to camp that night, but laid out our sleeping bags on the floor of the sitting room. Finally, I was back in the house. It was all very much as I remembered it. The piano in the corner which my grandmother had played. The old green sofa, where I used to hunt for coins which had fallen between the cushions. The huge window looking out to sea, where the dog would sit for hours.

I wanted to dance from room to room, to yell out for joy in escaping the mountain, in finding again my lost home, in resurrecting the dead. To delight in the peaty yellow water which flowed from the taps in the bathroom. The scattered photographs from my childhood in the hall. My grandfather's binoculars still sitting on the window sill.

All too soon this was to end. I left that house for the final time that day. And perhaps from the corner of my eye, I could see my grandmother standing at the front door, smiling, waving, disappearing into the dark. I longed to bury my face in her little dog's fur, as she sat in my lap. Instead I turned my face to the night, and let silent tears roll down my cheeks.

In the end, it is not boots or cars or ferries, it is only our minds, our stories that can take us back home.

September

The year's dying on its feet
she said, making me think
of my mother.

No matter how her head hurt
or her heart laboured
she kept going.

Kept going. Dying on her feet.

And the year will keep going
paying out days, reeling in light
failing, faltering, fading

until in the dark it gives out.

Make Believe

Rainbows of silk and muslin
hang on the line, colours brightened
by strong sunlight.
Generations of children
have draped their lives with these squares
imagining themselves on pirate ships
or deep in woodland; scouring beaches
or trapped in towers.
Their airy lightness made homes
whose walls and roofs
softened a harsh world, carried it
out of consciousness
to be transformed again
in the span of a mayfly.

J M Alderson

Summer Daybreak, Isle Of Lewis

Above a hillock
below deep grey cloud lines
a patch of intense gold
shades out to streaks of red.

Upturned boats
wait on grassy tussocks
where river meets sea
in a shimmer of grey and silver silk.
Reflected light
strikes pink and white pillars
deep into water.

Sheep and cattle wade
in tides of silverweed, sorrel, sow-thistle.
They raise voices now and then
to join the cry of gulls,
the peep of oystercatchers.
Somewhere close
a cormorant calls.

Shadows lift and lay hills
in patterns that range
from green to grey to black
while sun climbs high and white
sending long rays through cloud.
The legs of my own shadow
stretch before me in the road.

Robina McCandlish

The Island

It was grand to walk along the shingled beach with Granny of an evening, inspecting pieces of drift-wood and conical shells washed up by the tides. We'd sit on the flat rock and watch the sun sink below the horizon, and I'd listen to Granny as she wove her many tales, the content of which she declared were, "As true as I'm sitting right here beside you, Dod." Mesmerised, I'd hear her talk of the Seal People or Selkies, who, she said, could ofttimes be seen bathing and frolicking around the shores of our island.

"The Selkies are right bold. Sure, they hide their own true coverings away under the rocks along the shore, before walking the land among us human folk."

And with a far-away look in her eyes, she'd tell me, "Such handsome creatures, the Seal Men are, that they've been known to turn the head of many a human maiden, just as the Seal Women have winsome ways to capture the heart of any poor unsuspecting male they might look upon, whether he be spoken for or otherwise."

Granny's tales enthralled me, and from a young age I had a natural curiosity of the sea and its creatures. Hungry for more knowledge, I'd ask, "How is it these Selkie folks are able to do this if they belong in the ocean? And why is it I've never seen them walk upon the shore?"

"Would you know if you had seen them in human form, for wouldn't they look the same as you and I," Granny would come back at me.

I'd gaze out at the bobbing heads of the seals. As they stared back at me with their soft human-like eyes, I'd wonder if Mhairi O'Connor was a Selkie in disguise, for had she not made my heart flutter wild in my chest when she kissed me full on the mouth as we played around the Standing Stones.

Granny had a tale about almost everything on the island. If I played hide-and-seek in the ruins up on Cluthie Hill with Willie and Mhairi O'Connor, I had to set off home before dusk, for when the light begins to fade that's when the Fairy Folk come up from their underground kingdom. Everybody knows, if you accidentally were to spy a Fairy at play, you would be stolen away by them, never to be heard of again.

Willie and Mhairi knew this to be true for hadn't their parents told them the same tale.

A rainbow too, was another mystical thing Granny knew about.

125

"Folks have a common belief there's a pot of gold at the end of the rainbow owned by the Fairy Folk and guarded by the King of the Leprechauns himself. That's not strictly so, Dod," she'd tell me, her eyes serious as they peered into mine. "You hear of people chasing rainbows, but no one ever catches one. The truth is, a Rainbow is something very precious. You see, Dod, it's a bridge betwixt our world and the next. One day we'll all get to cross over that bridge and maybe that day will be not too far off for your auld Granny. When I'm gone, look for me in the Rainbow, for it's there I'll be, watching over you." And she'd smile and ruffle my hair.

I could never imagine Granny going anywhere, but still I wondered why it was she who looked after me, why it was I didn't have a Mammy and Daddy, like Willie and Mhairi? I wondered about it but never had the courage to ask, for I feared there was something I wasn't supposed to know.

But tonight as we sat there on the flat rock, there was a deeper fear in me. Tomorrow I would leave Granny and the island, to go to the big school on the mainland. I breathed deep and plucked up the courage to ask out loud, "Why is it that you look after me, Granny? Why am I not the same as Willie and Mhairi O'Connor?"

"In what way are you not like the O'Connors? Sure do they not have a Granny too, our Dod?"

"Aye, and they have a Mammy and Daddy as well, so where is my Mammy and Daddy?"

There, I had boldly asked the question that for so many years had burned inside of me.

Granny's lined face turned and looked deep into mine, quiet-like. Then she got up from the flat rock and walked down the beach to the water's edge. For a long moment she watched the ebb before she turned and said, "You're twelve gone, laddie, and it's the summer's end. Tomorrow you're away over the water to board in the big school. My heart, it breaks, for I'll maybe never again look upon your fair face. I suppose it's only right, before you go, you hear the truth from my own lips."

I sat motionless, the fear burning in me.

Granny didn't come and sit down on the rock but stayed staring over the ocean. Then she said:

"Your Mammy was the fairest lass on the whole of the island, but she was a discontented being from a young age. As she grew, so did her yearnings for things other than what she had. I put blame on magazines brought over from the mainland, for filling her head with thoughts and daydreams of faraway

126

places. She tried the patience of us sorely, her Dada and me. When she left for the school just as you're about to, her absence was replaced by serenity, and though we loved our lassie greatly we treasured the calm place our home had become.

"When she returned, she had grown even bonnier, but also more disgruntled than ever before. Her work on the dyeing of the wool was done with a grudging heart and her foot on the pedals of the loom unwilling. How could one so fair of face be so unhappy with her lot? Dada and I asked each other, but deep down we knew the answer."

Granny walked up the sand and sat down heavily beside me on the rock. Her old face crumpled as though she was going to weep and that fear of knowing bit into me again and I wanted to tell her to stop, it didn't matter. But she sighed deeply and gripped both of my hands between her rough brown fingers and said:

"Your Mammy wasn't my true daughter, Dod. I never birthed her." Her sad eyes bored into my face. "You have the same look as your Mammy, the same soft dark eyes. You see, Dod, I found her right here by this very rock we're sitting on. I was collecting the seaweed and gorse to use for the wool dyeing, and in the shelter of the rock wrapped in a soft pelt there was this tiny wee thing, all alone for there was not another soul on the beach."

I understood, for had I not seen the animals give birth many times over, but this was different, I felt different, and a lump grew in my throat as I saw Granny's eyes mist over.

It was a minute before she spoke again, as though to herself. "When I saw that it was a bairn so newly born, I cried, for was it not my dearest wish to have a child. Had I not come down here month on month and year on year on the tide's ebb, my tears mingling with the ocean, crying out to have a child of my own? I thought my prayers had been answered, and took the wee one home to show Padraig, but he told me to put it back where I'd found it.

"It was winter and the snows were due but I had to do what my husband bid. I fed the poor wee creature goat's milk and wrapped it in a newly spun plaid to keep it warm. For seven days and seven nights I checked on the baby and fed it the milk, waiting all the while for the Mither to appear, but she never came and I convinced myself the child was left as a gift to me from the Sea, from a Selkie woman, maybe.

"When spring came and we were able to get about the island again, everyone congratulated Padraig and me for at last making a baby, for we were not young. We adored our lovely daughter as we watched her grow, though at times she tried us sorely."

Granny took her gaze from me and looked out over the darkening waters. When she spoke again, a smile played on her face.

"One day Padraig came in from the peat fields and said he had seen our daughter on the shore with a young man. We were relieved that at last she had maybe found the happiness she craved, and for a while she had. We listened as her sweet voice echoed over the hillside and along the meadows as she gathered the heather and bracken. She sang while working the loom and she grew more radiant as the days and weeks passed. Each evening she'd slip away out to see her true love and we'd hear her singing on her return.

"One evening she didn't come back. Though we were old, we remembered our courting and her Dada and I smiled each to the other and went to bed. Next morning when she still hadn't returned, we went out to look for her. By the side of the flat rock we found *you*, not long born, wrapped in her petticoat. A note simply said she knew we would understand she had gone, back to her own folk. 'As payment for the love bestowed on me,' she wrote, 'I leave you my son. He is called Dod.'

"Padraig was broken-hearted and set off in the boat to find her. Neither of them returned. Bereft though I was, I had you to care for."

In silence we sat side-by-side on the flat rock, Granny and me, and watched the red ball of the sun disappear.

As we took the path back to the cottage, I looked at the stars hanging low in the velvety black sky. Gone was the fear I'd carried for so long but in its place was a feeling of strangeness and an overwhelming excitement.

Next morning, as the boat slipped away from the jetty, I waved to the lone figure of my Granny. I still felt excitement but mingled with this was sadness, for I knew I would not see her again. With this knowledge came pain so deep in me I had to turn away. Facing the swell of the sea and the mainland I saw the beautiful arc of a rainbow, bright in an overcast sky, and remembered what Granny told me about it being a bridge between this world and the next. Tears wet on my face, I felt her comforting presence, and knew that, whatever the future held, I would one day return to the island, the place of my birth.

Brahmaputra

On the Brahmaputra fishermen still throw nets —
these days their catch is meagre
for not many fish are left.
Larger boats ferry sand
dug from banks already eroding
to build a bridge to *Somewhere*.

The waters of the Brahmaputra —
they come from *Somewhere*,
from mountains far away, they say,
and feed the mountains into the Bay.

But I am here, not there, not *Somewhere*,
and here the fish do not bite.
Too much of someone else's mountain
muddies our water and the fish have gone.
Instead, the river eats into our homes
and carries them, along with the mountains,
down to the Bay.

On the Brahmaputra I ride the boat
that hunts the fish that have swum away.
The catch is small and we shall not eat much tonight.
Maybe I, too, should go *Somewhere*
and leave the river behind.
But I cannot go to the mountains
for they are being washed away,
and I cannot go to the sea
for my boat is too small.
I am here, not *Somewhere*,
and here the fish will not bite.

The Brahmaputra still flows by as he has always done.
One day he will take my house to the Bay
and then finally he will have won.

Bryan Owen

Stamp River Falls

The waters surged through the ancient forest
excited, disturbed and turbulent
as they tumbled over rocks
and smacked hard against boulders
carelessly tossed and littered long ago.

The channel narrowed.
The river thundered and swirled
as it was forced into the gorge —
all spindrift and scouring danger —
and the roar filled our ears.

Birds flitted from shore to shore
catching insects on the wing.
Trees leaned over and watched
for they had seen it all before.

When we have finished destroying the earth
for a mess of dollars and a pottage of pride
the waters of the driven, riven, river
will still tumble down to the sea.

In that day birds will still flit and salmon will spawn;
the waters will crash and smash as they do today
and all will be as it was before.

And there will be respite —
until selfish genes create selfish creatures
and waters flow out of a new Eden
and head for a new Fall.

Bryan Owen

The Broomielaw

We walked along the Broomielaw,
my love and I, her arm in mine and mine in hers,
thinking on times past and long ago
of ships and luggers and men uncouthie
tobacco and fish unloading
and coffee and tea —
cargoes that made rich men rich
until their ships foundered on a distant shore
when rich men became poor
and rued the day
they first went doon the Broomielaw.

We walked along the Broomielaw,
my love and I, her arm in mine and mine in hers,
listening to the shouts of men long dead
who in their turn had led their ladies,
wives or mistresses along Jamaica Street
to dark inns darkened by hard men home
after long voyages over oceans rough.
Then tough men spending their wages on hoors and ale
paled into silence as Glasgow's rain,
Glasgow's lashing rain, washed the ghosts away
while my love and I walked doon the Broomielaw
not so long ago.

Angus D H Ogilvy

Anent the Kirk's Intent Anent Anent

Tak tent! Tak tent!
The kirk's hell-bent on proscribin' anent.

Lang syne it's scrieved in holy writs
tae document hoo 'oors were spent
in convocation.

Bit noo it's no' got God's consent,
and so they're like tae scrieve:
'concerning' —

which isnae hauf an apt intent
fur nae'ne o' them kent
whit 'anent' meant!

*(In May 2013 the General Assembly of the Church of Scotland was told that the word
'anent' would be removed from all church documents to make them more accessible.)*

Angus D H Ogilvy

Jambanja

With the darkness come the drums, and the numb cries
culled from ganja and chibuku round the fires
they've stoked with wooden toys and books on husbandry.

Such blazing starshine, sweet with smoke, defines
the shadows of the broken ridgebacks on the lawn,
the splayed form of the farmer flayed with knobkerries.

The hamstrung bull lies bleating on its bloodied knees;
black pangas hack the avenue of trees.

This year a bumper harvest was foretold:
ripe crops of clothes and bedding; plucked mementos;
scattered windmills; ripped out plumbing; gathered souls;

the chaff of lives whose stories would turn cold
before the torching of the thatch,
the resurrected ghosts from charring bones.

('Jambanja' is a Shona term meaning 'violent overthrow'.)

Angus D H Ogilvy

The Road To Mellon Udrigle

It's always that bit further than you think;
selective memory eradicates
this and that dull dip or undistinguished hump,
the extra mile of dun, dry grasses.

It entices you with glimpses of
a blue-green sea, a blackbird on a fence post
with a pink worm wriggling in its amber beak,
flares of gorse flower sharp as mustard
on the grey dregs of a wintered hill,
the russet limbs in one last stand of pine.

As the light intensifies, I follow the salt
towards the machair on the one track road
that winds and ducks and swings through boulders
cast by vanished ice, defer at passing places
to the slothful coming back, expect that
it should be around the next bend, or the next.

Mary Edward

Lunch At The Palazzo

It's his first time in the bistro and he's not impressed. The Venetian Lagoon on the mural is cracked and faded, and Vesuvius is never going to erupt again on that grimy wall. The once-cheerful tablecloths have been washed a hundred times too often, and the menu wilts in his hand.

He's surprised that Sam Deasey would choose this place for their meeting. Then he looks around at the empty tables and has his answer.

The shabby black shoes of the waiter catch his eye, and he follows their shuffle around the room. The old man's feet must be bad. He glances down at his own polished Barkers. At least he still has some decent footwear. He watches the waiter to avoid watching the door. He can't afford to look anxious.

A couple come in and sit near Anthony. The waiter, his body an obsequious question mark, leans in to take their order and a lock of grey hair falls on to his brow. He brushes it aside wearily with the back of his hand, and Anthony sees his own father. In the end he was exhausted too.

Passing, the waiter raises his eyebrows, but Anthony shakes his head. "Meeting someone." He takes a dusty-looking breadstick to show he's fine. The waiter shuffles off to the kitchen just as Sam Deasey arrives on a wave of cold air.

"Tony." He holds out his hand.

Anthony half-rises to shake Deasey's hand and feels moisture — his or the other man's he can't tell. Deasey looks like a banker. He shrugs off a dark overcoat and the suit is conservative. Anthony knows what bankers look like; he's had his fill of refusals from men in suits like this. His heart sinks.

But it rises again when the chunky gold bracelet slides from beneath the jacket sleeve. He's forgotten for a moment what Deasey actually is a money-lender, plain and simple. You can take the boy out of the slums but you can't take the... Anthony hides a smile at the memory of wee Sammy in his trackie-bottoms running errands for the hard men, and hustling Anthony's dad in the chippy late at night for the burnt crumbs left in the fryer. But that was thirty years ago. Now he's a fat man in a banker's suit, his loud aftershave drowning out the garlic. And Anthony needs him.

The waiter does his version of hurrying over. Deasey opens his arms wide. "Marco — bring my usual — and whatever my friend here wants."

Marco hovers. Anthony has no appetite and the waiter seems to know this. "Just some bread? Some olives?"

Anthony nods.

"Right, Tony." Deasey crunches on a breadstick. "What can I do for you?"

"I've got a problem. Cash flow."

The waiter bumps a carafe of red wine down on the table, and little splashes land on the cloth. They look like bloodstains.

"Cash flow!" Deasey laughs; there's a shred of breadstick, like cardboard, caught in his teeth. "All right, what's the story?"

The story? It's the one about the idiot who flew too high and had the wings melted off him. His father had tried to warn him about the hard choice he was making, but was he going to listen to an old guy who could only fry chips? Was Antonio Franchi going to waste his life getting up at four o'clock every morning to freeze in the fish market, then slave until midnight every night frying haddock? And the fat. On his skin, in his sweat — maybe even in his blood. The embarrassment when his dad came to the school and the smell filled the space around them.

His mother had agreed, and Anthony went to college to study business administration. And there met Alicia. Her father was a stockbroker. He smelled of money.

"Come on, Tony. Give. What happened to the wine shops?"

The waiter comes back, balancing Deasey's spaghetti dish in one hand and the bread basket and olives in the other. He peers into Anthony's face and frowns, then turns with a little stagger back to the kitchen. Anthony points with his thumb. "What's *his* story?"

Deasey twirls his spaghetti. "Marco? Re-development. Did okay till all the houses and offices buggered off." He tilts his head. "You must have clocked the spaces."

A row of shops left in a wasteland: a pub, closed — a laundrette, closed — then The Palazzo, barely alive in its concrete coffin. The old guy himself not much better.

Anthony takes a deep breath. "Okay, Sam."

"About bloody time." Deasey looks at his watch. "I've got other fish to fry, you know." The barb is unintended. He's not clever enough.

"The wine shops. Going into administration any day soon."

Deasey's eyes narrow. "What kind of money would that take?"

"No... No. It's too late for the business. It's the house."

"Repossessed?"

Anthony wipes his brow with his gritty napkin. "Not yet. But soon, if I don't get..."

Deasey leans back, savouring his mouthful of wine. "I'd need security."

"I've still got the Range Rover. That's worth..." He stops as Deasey almost chokes with laughter.

"Tony, my son, they're ten a penny!"

"What?"

"Sure. I can get you one for a couple of grand."

"But it's almost new, and it cost..."

Even when he bought it he knew they couldn't afford it. But Alicia wanted it for towing the horsebox. Ideally, she said, she'd like a transporter, but she knew things were a bit tight. Even her dear old dad had pulled back after his bank crashed. No help there for Anthony's wine shops.

It had been so good for a while. One shop was a start but he wanted a chain. And when he died, the money his dad left him began to make that dream come true. Alicia's father had the contacts — people who knew their wines. But when that world began to crumble — well, supermarkets sell wine, don't they?

Deasey is speaking. "The house, duh?"

Anthony blinks. "What about the house?"

"Come on, don't act stupid!" The thick lips are twisted. "Your bloody wine shops are up the creek, so I'll have your house as security if I lend you the cash."

The banker is fast disappearing.

The house, with its stable-block, is Alicia's project since she doesn't need to work, and she basks in its gleaming perfection. Anthony feels ice pour into his stomach. Alicia's beautiful house? Lost to a thug like Deasey?

A month ago it was unthinkable that they should sell the house, but that was before the bank put pressure on the mortgage. If Deasey saves the day Alicia won't have to know how close to the abyss they've come. Not yet, anyway.

The waiter asks if they want coffee. When he leaves, Anthony says, "Wouldn't the developers buy him out?"

Deasey grins. "Sure, but the old fool wouldn't take it."

"For God's sake, why not?"

"Look, forget Marco — you're the mug in trouble here."

Anthony looks around the shabby restaurant, at the waiter's black trousers with the sheen of old age, and his painful feet. He shakes his head. "I don't get it."

Deasey sits up and leans his fat face into Anthony. "You'll not get it either if we don't talk business." His eyes follow Anthony's to the waiter. "Didn't like the developer. Some crap about his principles, he said." He slaps the table.

137

"Principles? Who the hell needs them? Now, listen Franchi, the deal. How much?"

Anthony feels sick at the prospect of putting his misery into figures for a guy like Deasey. Sammy's kind wouldn't have got within a mile of his select wine-tastings. Sure, there were con-men galore at his parties, but they moved in high places and could hide in their Armani suits. And they never wore thick gold bracelets.

"How much?" Deasey's eyes bore into him and he flaps his big wallet like a fan. It's as if he can read Anthony's mind.

Marco arrives with the coffee as Deasey says, "Okay. I'm going to the bog. If you don't tell me how much you want by the time I come back, I'm out of here." He puts the wallet away. "And you'll be skint."

The waiter bends over with the tray, slowly arranging the cups and saucers and a bowl of sticky sugar cubes. He mutters something which Anthony doesn't catch.

"Sorry?"

The waiter straightens up. Pulls back his shoulders. "Dirty money." He whips his napkin over Deasey's place. "Very dirty money."

Anthony sits there, stunned. It is several minutes before Deasey returns to the table, wiping the edge of his hand under his nose. "Okay, you've had time to think, Franchi. How much?"

"Yeah, Sam... Time to think. And I don't want your money." He gets up. "But I'll let you pay the bill, seeing I'm skint."

Outside, he decides he'll sell the Range Rover to a garage, then contact an estate agent. Walking up the broken street he searches his pockets, finding several worn banknotes, a handful of coins — and a couple of principles he'd forgotten he had.

through fog a horizon

through fog a horizon
the horizon an illusion
beyond, more sea, sky, land
beyond, back to where we started

all paths
lead back
be still
the world turns
and you move

no path
no search
where you are
all life will come

the water

the water
reflects colours
that are spread around it
glistens in light
cool to my lips
my mouth
soothes my dry throat
impels gratitude
from the quenched cup

A Colder Kiss

When Sarah was nine, her brother, Gordy, died.

Gordy was twelve and had been ill for months, struck down by a sickness none of the adults, doctors or nurses could identify. People came to see him — specialists, priests, faith-healers — all made the long journey to the village. None of them knew what was wrong. No-one knew what to do. He was prodded, tested, prayed-over, spiked with needles to draw his blood. It was useless. Gordy lay in bed, surrounded by toys, games and comics — the trivial things visitors brought to cheer him. He didn't even bother to pick them up. He rarely moved, and never spoke.

Gordy's bed was tucked into a corner of his room. Beside it, a small, round table rested against the wall with a lopsided lamp sitting on top, its shade yellowed and tattered with age. A rug with a worn pattern of sad, sorry animals covered the raw floorboards, and an ancient trunk with tarnished brass hinges squatted under the window like a patient pet.

Sarah watched from her chair in the opposite corner, in the shadow cast by the oak wardrobe. She watched the adults come and go; their bustling fuss as they tried to make Gordy better; their breezy false laughter as they swept into the room, attempting to lift his spirits with their weak jokes, their funny stories, each of them hoping with a quiet desperation that they would be the one to trigger some miracle recovery.

Gordy's frailty only increased.

Winter came, and the wind roared around the little wooden house, causing the windows to shudder and boom. Draughts crept in under the door, sending dustballs, like the ghosts of mice, scurrying across the bare floor beneath Gordy's bed.

The days grew shorter and Sarah kept her vigil. She came home from school each day, ate her meal and helped the adults with the dishes and other chores before climbing the stairs to Gordy's room, where she sat silently in the cold darkness of the far corner. She watched, while the adults made their noises downstairs, talking and banging in the kitchen or the hall. Now and then, the sound of the radio set drifted up from the living room, a thin, bleak music that gave no cheer. Gordy's eyes would sometimes glitter in the dim glow from the bedside lamp and Sarah thought he wept quietly then. She did not comfort him.

On some days, after school, she would be sent to the village on an errand. There would be enquiries from the shopkeepers and neighbours, and Sarah would be polite and tell them nothing had changed. The women, in their plain white aprons and headscarves, would smile sadly and shake their heads. A few might whisper to each other, slyly covering their mouths, and, hard as she tried, Sarah could never quite catch their words. Mister Garland, the grocer, a ponderous oak of a man with thick bottle-glass spectacles and a drinker's nose like a burst pomegranate, would take her hand and stroke it clumsily, telling her not to worry, everything was going to be fine.

It would be dark when she returned home and she carefully picked her way along the lane that ran between high, gnarled trees. The house crouched in the distance beneath cold, bright stars suspended in the terrible deep. The downstairs curtains would be drawn, but the light from Gordy's window shone into the night — a pale diamond, fragile and alone.

When the end came, it seemed to Sarah that Gordy just faded. The adults had come in and fixed his blankets and pillows, fluffing and rearranging them, making him more comfortable. They had gone over to the window, talking in hushed tones, their backs to the room.

Sarah was in her chair, watching Gordy.

His eyes were open, staring at the ceiling, and his arms lay outside the covers, stiff and brittle like bleached sticks. Sarah felt a transformation in the air — it seemed to thicken, become heavier, and the adults' voices receded to the edge of hearing. Gordy's eyes fluttered once, then closed. His chest gave a soundless heave and settled quietly into the bed in a long, slow deflation.

Sarah held her own breath. When it began to hurt and she could no longer keep it in, she pointed to the bed and said, "*See.*"

The adults turned and looked, following her finger.

They blinked and stared, their faces pale and uncomprehending; then they flew into a sudden storm of grief and weeping and guilt. They held fast to each other and wailed and collapsed across Gordy's bed, crushing him with their weight. Not that Gordy could feel them.

Sarah sat in the corner until the adults exhausted themselves with their sobbing and pulling of their hair. She waited till they left Gordy in his room, retreating downstairs to the kitchen to make tea, to telephone relatives and neighbours, to let them know what had happened, to make arrangements.

Sarah stood slowly, and went to Gordy's bed. She bent close and examined the small details of his face — the tiny pits and pocks around his nose, the black wires of his eyebrows, the little crust of dried tears at the corners of his eyes.

Sarah moved her face close to his. She closed her eyes, brought her lips down onto Gordy's open mouth and sucked.

She sucked hard.

She drew in the last of the air from his lungs, absorbed the final molecules that his failing body had produced.

She stepped back from the bed.

She knew what she had done.

Resplendent

It was tough at the top,
hot — too hot to handle,
flames licking around her feet,
walking on fire.
Up here it seemed worth it,
a view to die for.
Below, fire ants dancing
demented as sand
on a drum skin.
From dust tumbling like snow,
crackle of tinder wood
and glowing embers,
she kindled enthusiasm,
reborn in instant spark,
turning plumage
this way and that,
iridescent in the setting sun.
She considered choices,
spread out her limbs,
let them admire, applaud;
bowed once, resplendent,
rose from her eyrie ashes
and soared to the heavens.

Game On

On that oblong pitch,
grass as fresh and close cropped
as a skinhead's three day rough,
players, like spilled beads
from an unstrung necklace,
scatter chasing the pearl egg
across the heady turf.
It pings off boots,
kicking the wanton pebble
skimming over and thru
curved air, into the
hair-net like a nit
in a fine toothed comb.
Lines score the ground
into quadrants and zones,
like the markings on
a monastery cloister,
where the rule of
walking is relaxed
and the tonsure forgotten.
In the stands, the lice
sway and seethe in
perpetual motion,
jostling, whilst the pearl
seeks to be strung from
one or other exotic necklace
and should it hatch,
either infestation would
be exultant and no-one
dares to mention Referee.

Pete Stuart

Caucus

Bracken cracks the shale
fringing the dunescape folds.
Grass ice softening
as the days lengthen.
Ahead red setter lopes
into a conference
of gulls. We're
close enough to hear
their chagrin
as they wheel out
over wolf-grey sea
to resume the caucus
a furlong up the strand.

Pete Stuart

En Prise

At the point
where white slab
of gable end
meets terracotta chippings,
a hint of earth, a speck,
sustains a flimsy stem,
trembling corrola
of recursive petals.
En prise
but such a plucky blue.

In For A Penny

Ah thoat a helicopter crash wid be a pretty hellish thing. Ah mean, it wis an that, but it wisnae as bad as Ah expectit.

God knows whit caused it. Aw Ah know is that wan meenit we're oan the wey hame fae the site, me an big Fergus, flying ower the Canadian forest. Miles an miles ae it. Couldnae see where it ended. Next thing, there's a fucker ae a bang an we're spinnin aboot, big three hunner an sixty degree turns, an the sky an the trees are aw mixed up wi wan anither. Fergus wis yellin his lungs oot, but Ah jist hung oan tae ma sait. Ah wis shitin it aw the same. Don't let me kid anybidy intae thinkin Ah'm some sorta cool bastirt that thinks nothing ae a helicopter crash. Naw, no me. As Ah say, Ah held oan tae ma sait, but inside Ah wis aw gaun.

The pilot wis brilliant, by the way. Managed tae control the thing a wee bit, stoap the spinnin. But it wis too late. We were too near the trees an we startit clippin the taps ae them. Well, that wis it. We nose dived an the rotors sliced through the branches an broke aff. We plunged doon intae the grun right beside a wee burn. Of coorse Ah didnae take that wee detail in at the time. Naw, Ah wis too dazed. Ah'd bumped ma heid aff the side windae, but that wis the full extent ae ma injuries. Made me feel a wee bit woozy, but that wis aw.

Fergus, well he wis still screamin. "Oh ma leg! Ma leg! Jesus, Mary an Joseph," an aw stuff lik that. Ah suppose it was broken or somethin. The pilot, though, well he wis deid. Ye could tell right away. He wis slumped ower the controls, an his erms were at a weird angle. Ah unclipped masel fae the seatbelt an crawled furrit tae have a luk at him. Wantit tae make sure he wisnae jist unconscious or somethin. But naw, the guy wis away.

The chopper wis lyin nose-doon, so Ah hud tae climb back up the flair tae get tae Fergus. By noo he had stoaped the screamin, but he wis greetin.

"C'moan big man," Ah says, "we need tae get oot ae here. In case she blows." Christ, Ah sounded lik a bloody action hero or somethin. But it seemed lik the kinna right thing tae say at the time.

Onywey, Ah went tae help Fergus get oot ae his seatbelt. He wis moanin an groanin an when a telt him tae unbuckle hissel he luked at me funny an says, "Ah think ma fingers are broken. Baith hauns." He held them up. The fingers were bent funny right enough.

"Can ye move them?" Ah asks.

"Naw," he says, an starts greetin harder.

Ah couldnae staun that kinda thing. No in a man. Ah mean Fergus is a big guy, six feet somethin. Tae see him lik a wee wean or a wummin wis jist hard tae stomach. Don't get me wrang, Ah'm no tryin tae offend wimmen or onythin, it's jist that ye mibbe expect it a bit mair fae them, but no a big beardy bastirt lik Fergus.

Ah unbuckled him, an, sufferin Christ, because ae the wey the helicopter wis lyin, did he no slip furrit intae the back ae the pilot's chair. Well! Ah thoat the greetin wis bad? Ye shoulda heard him wance his sair leg hut the metal stanchion behin the chair. Ah never thoat a man wid be capable ae makin noises lik that.

Ach, there wis nuthin fur it, but tae haul him oot ae there, screamin in agony or no. He couldnae staun up right, so Ah hud tae pull him oot ae the side door an ontae the grun ootside. Ah pulled him as faur away fae the chopper as Ah could, an dumped him aginst an auld tree trunk.

Wance Ah'd goat him settled, Ah hud a luk aboot the place. The trees were really dense. Except fur the wans that the chopper hud demolished, they were thick as onythin as faur as ye could see. Made walkin through them near impossible.

Fergus wis slumped semi-conscious aginst the tree an wis mumblin tae hissel. Ah shook his shooders. "Fergus! C'moan, wake up!" He lifted his heid, his eyes aw glessy-like. He wis droolin aw doon his shirt. "Fergus! Stey awake! Don't you go unconscious oan me!" Ah went doon tae the wee burn an soaked an auld rag a hud in ma poaket. Ah took it back up an wrung it oot ower Fergus's heid. He came roon a wee bit mair.

"Ma fingers. Ma legs..." he slurred.

"Listen," Ah says, "Ah need tae try an fun oot where we ur. Wait here, Ah'm gaun back tae the chopper." He luked intae ma eyes, strugglin tae focus.

"Whit aboot the pilot?" he asked.

Ah shook ma heid. Fergus blinked a couple of times an sniffed back a big snotter.

"Did he save us?" he asked.

Ah luked at the chopper an the mess aw roon aboot us.

"No yet," Ah replied.

Ah scrambled ower tae the helicopter, still a wee bit wary that it might explode. There wis only the wee quiet tickin sound as the engine cooled doon an a smell ae fuel. The front wis pretty smashed up an ye could see that the pilot musta took the full brunt ae the impact. The cabin windae wis shattered an aw the electronics were hingin oot ae the panels, the dashboard rammed right up aginst the pilot's legs, an Ah could see they were crushed tae buggery.

Ah rummaged through the instruments tae see if Ah could fun the radio, but Ah didnae know whit it would luk like. Ah clambered up beside the pilot an pulled his heid back. He made a funny gurglin noise in his throat as his heid lolled back, but it wis jist his juices movin aboot inside him. Ah quickly fun the wire comin oot ae the microphone oan his helmet an traced it back doon tae the instrument panel. It plugged intae a dial thing wi some letterin oan it that didnae make any sense tae me. No that it maittered onywey. The hale thing wis ruined. The needles were aw broke an there were wires an stuff hingin oot ae it. Fuck it.

Ah began tae wunner if anybidy actually knew we would be missin. Ye see, we were flyin hame fae the site early. Me an Fergus were gonnae huv a few days boozin an livin it up in the toon afore we showed up hame in Scotland. Wur wives wid be nane the wiser.

But this made the broken radio aw the mair worryin. Naebidy wid really know we were away, an naebidy wid know whit route we were takin. Flyin low acroass remote countryside, flights lik this didnae register wi ony air traffic control centre or anythin. Probably aginst the rules fur aw Ah know. An there wis always a different nummer ae choppers sittin aboot the site that naebidy wid really know if wan had been booked oot, so tae speak. We could be missin fur ages an naebidy wid even think ae lukin fur us till God knows when.

Ah went back tae Fergus. He hudnae moved, but he wis a wee bit mair alert-lukin than before.

"Donny," he said, "can we get back? Is there a wey oot ae here? Will they fun us?"

Ah played it cagey-like, no sayin wan wey or the other whit Ah thoat wis gonnae happen.

"Donny," he said, "Ah need tae get tae a hoaspital. Quick. Ma leg's sair. Really sair. An Ah canny pick up or haud onythin. Ma fingers ur fucked."

Ah tried tae smile reassuringly at him.

Awright, Ah realise noo in retrospect that it probably luked lik a hideous sneer an Ah didnae mean tae gie him the jitters, but Ah wis mair than a bit taken aback when he started shoutin at me.

"Ye're gonnae leave me uren't ye, ya bastard! Ye're gonnae fun yer ain wey oot an leave me alane tae die!" His eyes were like a dug's baws, poppin oot his heid.

"Fergus, calm doon," Ah said, tryin tae luk concerned an as if the thoat hudnae croassed ma ain mind awready. "You're ma big buddy. Dae ye really think Ah'm the kinda guy that's gonnae run oot oan a mate? In a bad situation like this? No me big man! Me an you aw the wey!"

Ah'm no sure how convincin Ah sounded.

It started tae get daurk. Noo, Ah don't know if ye've ever spent any time oot in a big, thick forest at night. It's scary. There are *noises*. An it's as black as the Earl ae Hell's waistcoat. Ye cannae see a thing. Which makes the noises even mair frightenin. We knew that it wis jist animals scratchin aboot the place, but nevertheless it freaks ye oot, especially wi a deid boady no too faur away.

We stayed awake maist ae the night. He couldnae get tae sleep because ae the pain an Ah wis that het up by the hale day's events that sleep wis never gonnae come. We talked. Fergus wis concerned aboot how we were gonnae get oot ae this mess. It didnae luk too likely, Ah thoat, but didnae say it.

Later, Fergus voiced somethin that hud been at the back ae ma ain mind.

"Whit ur we gonnae dae for somethin tae eat?" he asked.

The thoat ae food hudnae occurred tae me in the first coupla oors efter the crash, but noo ma stomach wis feelin pretty damn empty. There wis nothin in the chopper, an we didnae even huv a chocolate bar atween us.

"Ah'll see if there's anythin in the forest that we could eat the morra," Ah said.

Fergus laughed for the first time that day. "Whit, are ye gonnae hunt an kill an animal or somethin?"

Ah laughed tae. Ah hudnae thoat this wan through, an we baith knew it. But the fact remained. We hud nuthin, an we would starve tae daith if help didnae come soon.

Efter another night ae tossin an turnin an coontin fuck knows how many fermyaird animals, Ah finally dozed aff. Ah woke up the next moarnin wi ma back in a crick. Fergus wis still sleepin. Ah didnae wake him, but crept away tae see if Ah could see anythin that luked promisin enough tae eat.

Ah came back wi seven worms an some nettley things that Ah'd hud a wee experimental nibble at. Fergus wis jist stirrin. Ah showed him whit Ah'd goat. He luked at me as if Ah hud two heids.

"Ur you serious?" he asked.

Ah nodded.

Ah don't know if ye remember cuttin up worms when ye were wee. But if ye dae, ye'll know that ye cannae really kill them. Or, at least when ye chop them up, each bit still wriggles aw oan its ain. Ah used tae think that the two bits grew new tails or heids an made two new worms. Mibbe they dae, Ah don't know enough aboot it. The thing is though... The thing is that when ye try tae kill a worm tae eat it, it's still kinda movin. The two ae us hud the dry boak when we tried it. Even worse, Ah got a bit stuck in ma teeth. An it wis *still* movin. Ah ran doon tae the burn an puked ma load. No that there wis much tae bring up.

When Ah got back tae Fergus, he wis lukin as grey as... Well, as grey as a really grey thing, Ah cannae think ae somethin tae compare him tae.

"Donny," he said, "Ah'm hungry, really hungry, but Ah jist cannae stomach that."

"Ah know whit ye mean," Ah said. "Well, whit ur we gonnae dae? You're no fit tae move, an that's aw a could fun oot there. There's hee-haw."

Fergus luked desperate.

We spent the rest ae the day maistly in silence. Ah hud a wee attempt tae climb wan ae the trees, tae see if a could see where we wur. The branches wur too tightly packed though, an Ah hud tae gie up. Ah searched through the chopper fur flares or anythin that could mibbe signal oor position.

Zilch.

But Ah did fun some rope, an a boax ae matches alang wi a couple ae duvet jaikets that we wrapped aroon oursels that night when we went to sleep.

The next day wis kinda borin. There wis bugger all tae dae. Fergus spent his time grumblin aboot his legs an fingers, which Ah must admit were gaun a funny colour, aw greeny-yella an that. But maistly we baith moaned aboot huvin nothin tae eat.

By the next day, it wis gettin really bleak. The weather wis gettin caulder an it startit tae rain a couple ae times. We hud plenty tae drink — the burn wis right beside us — but the two ae us were starvin. Ah could feel ma stomach gettin aw distended, an ma ribs were beginnin tae show — awright, mibbe Ah'm exaggeratin a bit fur dramatic effect.

We knew whit each other wis thinkin, but naither ae us wantit tae be the first tae suggest it. Ah waited till Fergus drifted aff intae wan ae his dozes an made ma wey ower tae the chopper...

When Ah came back, Ah woke Fergus an gave him two slender pieces ae raw meat. He didnae say anythin, but he took them onywey an gulped them doon.

152

Raw meat isnae nice. It's goat a sticky, fatty quality that clings tae the roof ae yer mooth an makes it hard tae swally.

Fergus luked at me. "It's him isn't it?"

Ah nodded. "Aye. It's aff his legs. They were aw crushed, made it easier tae get at it."

Efter the first day it wis easier. Ah mean, it wis still me that hud tae dae the butcherin, so tae speak, but Ah kinda shut ma eyes tae it aw. Ah yased a bit ae rotor blade that Ah'd retreived fae further up the hill. It wis jist the right size an sherp enough tae dae the job. Ah wid cut aff a wee bit ae meat an the baith ae us wid share it.

We'd completely loast track ae time when it came roon tae the days when we hud tae start eatin the bits we wurny too sure aboot. Fergus was gettin worse an he wis slippin in an oot ae consciousness durin the days noo. The thing wis though... Ah wis kinda gettin used tae the meat. Mair than that. Gettin tae like it. Sure, the pilot's boady wis beginnin tae smell a bit, an he wis gaun a funny colour, but, even so, Ah wis beginnin tae eat mair than ma fair share. Since it wis me that did the slicin an dicin, Fergus couldnae see that Ah snuck a few wee extra bits fur masel.

The pilot wisnae lukin like a man any mair. Maist ae his boady muscles were away by noo, an we were startin tae get doon tae the nitty-gritty. The bits that ye didnae want tae think too much aboot.

Like his willie.

He hud quite a big wan, an it seemed too much tae waste. Eftir aw, it wis meat jist like the rest ae him. An we wur awready in fur a penny...

Think ae it like a kinda tough beef olive. Wi a lot ae blood. That's whit a telt Fergus when he turned up his nose at it. But naw, he widnae touch it. So Ah ate it aw masel. Fergus widnae luk at the heart either, said it wis too much like eatin the essence ae the guy, whitever the hell he meant by that.

Ah stoaped gien him anythin efter that. He wis gettin worse by the day, an Ah wis the wan that hud the better chance ae survival noo. Ah needed tae keep ma strength up fur when the rescue boys finally turned up. It couldnae be too much longer noo. We must huv been oot here fur... How long hud it been? Ah couldnae tell. But that pilot wisnae gonnae last forever. Ah hud tae make some decisions.

There wis only wan thing fur it.

So, this is how Ah've ended up.

Fergus tied up aginst a tree, an me wi a sherpened dod ae helicopter

rotor blade in ma haun.
    Talkin tae masel.
    An it's nae yis him screamin. Naebody'll hear him.
    No oot here.

Rita Bradd

Perseids Watch

Now you see me. Now you don't.

I play the game. Tease.
Rent the night's blanket
for billions of needles and pins to mend
in the twinkling of an eye.

I see you

moulded in the grass,
flat on your backs.
Mother and son, eyes sunken
by the weight of binoculars.
Catching a wish.

Then. I'm gone.

Am I your future or your past?
Or just some stardust
chasing the tail of an ageing comet?
A riddle to be solved?

Or some heroic soul waving farewell
on my final journey?

(The Perseids are a meteor shower emanating from the debris of the comet Swift-Tuttle as it travels on its 133-year orbit of the sun. They are so-called because the point from which they appear to come [the radiant] lies in the constellation Perseus.)

Geoff Cooper

I Loved You So, On Facebook

From the first time I noticed
the photographs you posted
there was something in your look
I loved you so, on Facebook.

I loved you in Long Island
and then you said you moved
to a small town in Thailand,
then to somewhere in Peru.

I loved all those photo albums
no one prettier than you.
My friends said, "That's Denise van Outen
— nothing Photoshit can't do."

I thought you were a stoter of a lassie
sweet as tablet, sexy, sassy;
I loved you in Long Island and Peru
but I got it slightly wrong about you,
they tell me it's all porkie pies and fallacy
— you're just a balding barman in Barassie.

African Solstice

Here I know only
the sun is high all year
— it's a steep path to heaven.

When the light has found
every last darkness
every cool shadow,
I sometimes dream there are countries
where summer might gleam
with seed and soft rain;

I try to feed my children
with sunlight and moonlight;
we go to the well
where water is magic
— sometimes it's there
sometimes it's gone.

If my kids went to school
they would recite
the histories of the blessèd,
those who are remembered,
those who have water
as we have light.

I have heard, in darker places,
you talk of light so easily,
how the light reaches everywhere,
to your soul, to your heart,
deep under your soft skin.

Very soon, if you care to look,
you will know

the mercy of light
on our bones.

Serenissima (Venice)

As we wake, the images are born once more
from the water — light, that sudden angel,
announces orange-gold on palazzo and tower —
and Venus too rises, perfect, whimsical.

As I kiss you behind today's mask
our darker angels again discover
the body's cries do not ask
the provenance of lovers.

City, Goddess, infatuation, apparition,
endless icon, in the helpless complicity
of our closing eyes, in the oblivions
of ecstasy — discover our simplicity.

It is good. It is all we know. We blindly float
between the ripple and the shadow.

Hear The Angels Sing

"Oh, hush the noise, ye men of strife,
    And hear the angels sing."

Rosie managed to get to the end of the verse before another bout of coughing overtook her. She'd had the cough for days. It was getting worse. Every in-breath was painful and her ribs seemed to rattle when she breathed out. Her singing was little better than a croak.

It had turned out to be a better day than she had expected. Forced to abandon her favourite pitch outside Marks and Spencer — her voice couldn't compete with the newspaper vendor shouting the headlines about swans trapped in the frozen river — she had set herself up by the entrance to Debenhams. It was cold. The icy wind whipped down Queen Street and slammed into the bulk of the St Enoch Centre, but she hoped that people coming out of the stores laden with expensive gifts might pause and spare something for a woman singing carols. Her gamble paid off. The last minute Christmas shoppers were in charitable mood and she was pleased to see quite a few coins in the tin on the pavement in front of her.

As darkness fell and the crowds thinned, Rosie collected up the coins, stowed them safely into the pocket without a hole and set off towards the river. She was hungry and had enough money to buy something to eat and still have money left for later. The lights were still on in *Sid's Snax*. She pushed open the door and went into the steamy heat of the café. The smell of fried onions made her mouth water.

Sid was wiping down the surfaces and looked up as she entered.

"You're just in time," he said. "I was just about to close up. I don't think there'll be many more customers tonight. People have got better things to do on Christmas Eve, haven't they?"

Rosie nodded. "Aye, I suppose so," she said.

"What's it to be then?"

"A burger, please, and chips, and a mug of tea."

"Right you are, hen." He turned to the fryer. "Busy up the town is it?"

"Aye, it was mobbed. Quieter now though."

Rosie began to cough again.

"That's a nasty cough. Have you got something for it?"

She shrugged and said, "It's just a cough."

"There's a lot of it about just now. I blame the weather. Friggin' Baltic, so it is. They say it's twenty years since the Clyde froze over like this. And see, there's a pair of swans trapped in the ice. Poor buggers. I wouldn't like to be out there in this. Here's your tea, hen."

"Thanks."

Sid began to serve the food. While his back was turned, Rosie carefully measured four spoons of sugar into the mug and then popped another spoonful into her mouth.

"There you are. Tuck in." While Rosie ate, Sid continued, "The man from the Wild Swans League has been trying to free them but they keep attacking him. They're probably frightened. They can break a man's arm you know. Still, you can't just stand by and let the poor critters freeze to death, sure you can't? According to the news, he's going to have another go in the morning. That you done, hen? All right was it?"

"Grand, thanks."

"Good. You take care of yourself now and have a nice Christmas."

"Thanks, you too."

As she left the café, a blast of frosty air took Rosie's breath away and her emaciated frame was wracked by another bout of coughing. Not that anyone would have known how thin she was. Her spindly legs, in three pairs of holey socks and boots several sizes too big for her, were hidden beneath two skirts and a pair of trousers. On top she wore a blouse, a jumper, a fleece jacket and an ancient tweed coat so greasy that it could have stood up by itself. The ensemble was completed by a battered green felt hat and a soft silky scarf of indeterminate colour that she'd been given by — she couldn't remember who. She was wearing every garment that she possessed in an effort to protect herself from the cold. The rest of her belongings were packed into a tartan shopping trolley with wonky wheels, that she pulled along behind her wherever she went. Rosie had learned that it was wise to keep your stuff with you.

She headed down Stockwell Street towards Paddy's Market. It wasn't so much a market square as a triangle of waste ground bordered on one side by railway arches. Its jumble of scruffy stalls was much favoured by theatrical types in search of props and costumes, and by anyone wanting cheap fags or pirate DVDs. The detritus left at the end of the day when the stallholders had packed up was sometimes a source of something useful. Rosie hoped that none of the others had got there before her and was pleased to see that the area was deserted.

She was in luck. It looked as if everyone had been in a hurry to get home for Christmas. She didn't have to rake very deeply into the pile of discarded polystyrene cups and plastic packaging before she found a blanket. It was slightly damp and had a faint odour of urine but, delighted with her find, Rosie folded it carefully and placed it into the shopping trolley.

Cutting back onto Saltmarket, Rosie went into Victoria Wine. She'd already checked her money. There was enough left for a whole bottle of Buckfast. She decided that 'tonic wine' must be medicinal and would, therefore, do her more good than a six-pack of Special Brew.

Clutching the bottle inside the carrier bag she made her way down to the Clyde Walkway. She wasn't in the mood for company, so she avoided the area around the Salvation Army hostel, where she knew the other street people would be gathered, and walked instead towards the suspension bridge. Her breathing was laboured now and the icy air seemed to paralyse her lungs. She found a bench to sit on, opened the bottle and took a swallow. The liquid hit the back of her throat and made her cough. Another few mouthfuls seemed to sooth the cough, and she felt the warmth of the alcohol spread through her chest.

Rosie took her new blanket from the trolley and draped it round her shoulders. She stared across the river. The moonlight glinted on the frozen water and it seemed to her that a million glittering angels danced across its surface. As she pulled the blanket closer she noticed for the first time that it was pink, like the blanket on her bed at home when she was little.

No! She shook her head in an effort to make the memories go away. But they refused. She fingered the silky material round her neck. She remembered now. The nuns placed the white silky veil over her head on the day of her first communion. She sang a solo at the Mass. "Perhaps she'll have a vocation," they said. "She has the voice of an angel." Daddy had looked at her, in the white dress that Mammy had borrowed from a neighbour and with the white veil over her golden hair, and he said that she looked like one of God's own angels. But Rosie knew, even then, that daddies shouldn't do *that* to an angel. When her belly began to swell, Mammy called her a whore. Daddy said nothing and wouldn't look her in the eye. She was sent to the nuns. They said she was a sinner and would burn in hell. As soon as the baby was born they took it away. Rosie never saw it. Mammy said she'd brought shame on the family and wouldn't let her back in the house. Daddy still said nothing.

Since then she'd sung for her supper, and for the drink that kept the memories at bay. For some years she was popular in pubs and clubs, but eventually alcohol destroyed her looks and coarsened her voice. Her life spiralled downwards, until latterly she'd survived by busking and scavenging.

Exhausted by coughing and overwhelmed by memories, Rosie wrapped herself in the pink blanket and lay down on the bench. She tried to pray but couldn't remember beyond *Hail Mary, full of Grace*... So she did what she had always done. She began to sing.

> "...Peace on the earth, good will to men
> From Heaven's all-gracious King!
> The world in solemn stillness lay
> To hear the angels sing."

Rosie gasped for breath and the cold metallic taste of wine mingled with the warm saltiness of blood. As she exhaled, a red stain crept across the pink blanket.

On Christmas morning the news bulletin reported that Glasgow's weather was set to break records. The overnight temperature had plummeted to minus fourteen degrees Celsius and, for the second week in a row, all Premier League football matches had been cancelled.

There was jubilation that the swans trapped by the ice in the River Clyde had finally been freed as there were fears that they wouldn't survive another night in the freezing temperatures.

The body of a middle-aged woman had been discovered on the Clyde Walkway. The woman had not been identified. The police were not treating the death as suspicious.

Clipping

We discovered
after the long drawn-out going,
amongst his few private possessions
my father had kept a diary
of the year I was born.
No entries, not even on my birthdate
but a newspaper clipping
yellowing like teeth
a letter I had sent to a newspaper,
published and answered.
During years of apparent indifference
a quiet pride had lived within him.

Derek Parkes

Israel

Doctor Hans Weber,
Physician, Friend.
Connoisseur of fine cognacs on winter nights,
you comforted my Gabriele until the end,
delivered our sons into this foul world.
I joked that you would treat Hitler's piles
if he called upon your services.
You agreed, but said that you
wouldn't warm your hands.

They took you away
to treat the inmates of Theresienstadt
to fight their typhus with prayers.
I watched your vestments
burn in the street
your furniture, your effects, taken away
by horse and cart.
Then they fumigated the place
to destroy the 'infection'.

I miss our warm, close nights
our secular bond.
The chess games I could never win,
the arguments I always lost.
Your grand house and surgery is
occupied, now, by a Party quack,
that same Party that renamed you
Doctor Hans Israel Weber.
Physician, Jew.

Derek Parkes

Mother Tongue

Betty danced at The Games as a child
kicking and leaping to the swirl.
Her mother spoke Gaelic
to her friends,
English to everyone else
in pre-war, pre-tourist Port Ellen.
The years have taken away
her mother's tongue.
Robbed her
of its songs and stories.
Now she sits in the shelter
of her Glasgow accommodation
as her nephew visits.
His daughter dances reels
around the living room
stopping to impart the Gaelic
she's learning at school.
Candlelight
in the dark of the past.

Fifteen Minutes

I think the moon's exploded, Kerry says as she comes through the kitchen door, the one that opens up into the back garden.

What? I pick the wine bottle up from the table and look at the label. It's Merlot.

Look for yourself, she says. There's some sort of big halo and the moon looks all fuzzy.

All right, I say. I begin to roll a cigarette.

Hurry up, Kerry says.

What's the hurry I ask. I really don't think the moon's actually exploded.

I didn't say it had exploded. I said I *think* it's exploded. Kerry picks up her glass and drains it. This is nice. I hope you bought more than just the one bottle.

I point at a box on top of the fridge. I got six, I say. It was *buy two get one free.*

Not bogof?

Bogof yourself, I say. Come on. Let's see this exploding moon.

It's cold outside. I light my roll-up. There's not a lot of artificial light around here. It's a small estate bordering a golf course. The sky is dark but vividly starry and right in the middle, right in front of us, the moon looks as though it's exploded. There's a huge halo around it, perfectly round like a full moon, and it appears to be getting bigger, moving slowly outwards and certainly moving. The moon looks larger than it should be; and it's sort of hazy and dark where it shouldn't be, as if it's disintegrating.

Fuck, Kerry says. I was right. The fucking moon's exploded.

It can't have, I say. It must be some sort of optical illusion.

Really? Kerry asks. She sounds excited.

Pollution in the atmosphere, I say, more in hope than anything else.

What do you think caused it?

Caused what?

The fucking moon's exploded!

No it hasn't.

It certainly *looks* like it's fucking exploded.

Looks like. Not actually. I mean, how can the moon just explode?

So you don't think the moon's actually exploded, Kerry says, a bit agitated now — though that's probably at me and because of the wine, nothing to do whatsoever with what appears to be happening up in the sky. She's pointing up at the moon.

Look, I say, trying to be reassuring and realistic at the same time, the moon's not exploded. I look up to see a large chunk of it most definitely slide away from the body of the moon. Fucking hell, I gasp as if I've just been punched in the guts; I'm almost certain now that the moon's just exploded.

Kerry looks up at the chunk of moon. Fuck! she cries. The fucking moon's exploded! What the fuck do we do?

How the fuck should I know, I say as I push her back through the door. I slam the door shut then lock it.

Why are you locking the door? Kerry looks pale and she's biting her fingers.

I don't fucking know. It just seems a good idea. I cross the kitchen and take another wine bottle from the box on the fridge. My hand shakes — a lot — as I refill Kerry's glass. Wine splashes over the table. Fuck this, I say. I grasp the bottle in both hands and gulp down mouthfuls of wine.

The telly! Kerry runs into the living room and switches on the TV. What the fuck's this! I hear her cry out.

I run after her. What's going on? She's kneeling in front of the TV.

It's *Come Dine With Me*. Try a fucking news channel.

Kerry throws the remote at me. You find it!

I change the channel to the BBC news. It's unbelievable.

We watch the news as it tells us what we already know — the moon has exploded. The guy on the telly looks as if he's shitting himself:

No-one knows how or why but the moon has exploded. Errr...It seems bits of it have been blown into space. It, ah, looks very likely that bits of it will impact with the earth. Some of it will most probably burn up in the atmosphere but the larger pieces — errr — won't... I... Ah... Scientists are predicting that the main impact sites will be... Europe... North and central Africa... Errr... Western parts of Asia... Oh fuck...

Did he just say 'fuck'? Kerry asks.

The studio scene is replaced by a video of the moon. They've speeded it up so you can see the moon come apart. Now it looks like a plate that's been shattered; the moon isn't round anymore — it's a collection of shards and lumps flying apart.

The voiceover's a woman. Fifteen minutes, she keeps saying. First impact, western Europe, fifteen minutes.

Fifteen minutes for what, Kerry asks.

My mouth's dry so I take a slug from the wine bottle. It's still dry. Fifteen minutes, I manage to say, till the moon hits us.

What? Is the moon actually going to hit us? I mean, will it hit *us*? Maybe it'll miss or hit America instead.

I stare at Kerry. Surely she's taken this in? It's not going to miss, I say.

How the fuck do you know, she shouts.

Someone's hammering on our front door. The doorbell's ringing too. I take another swig from the wine bottle and go to see who's at the door. Kerry's shouting at me to come back.

I open the door. It's John, the guy who lives next door. I've never liked him; he's always moaning about the state of our garden or complaining that we leave our wheelie bin out on the pavement.

Hi, he says. Have you seen the news about... He falters. His eyes are wet. What do we do? he asks quietly.

Suddenly it all becomes blindingly obvious to me. The moon's just exploded and huge fucking chunks are about to crash into the earth at fantastical speeds. What do we do? Fuck all. We do fuck all.

Fuck off, I say and slam the door in his face. He rings the doorbell frantically and shouts and screams through the door. Kerry comes to see what's happening.

Who's that? She asks.

John.

John! John! Kerry presses her head against the door. Stop it or we'll call the police.

I'm suddenly filled with rage. I pull Kerry out of the way and yank the door open. Just fuck off, I scream in his face. There's fuck all anyone can do. Just fuck off.

John begins to weep like a baby. I close the door again.

Why did you shout at him? Kerry shouts at me. He's just scared.

It can't be more than three or four minutes since Kerry told me the moon had exploded. We've got fifteen minutes — probably less, thanks to the lying shits on TV — left to live before... Before what?

Fuck sake, I say out loud. Ten minutes or so, I say and walk past Kerry and into the living room.

I sit down in front of the TV. It's showing some outdated government bullshit about what to do in the event of a nuclear attack — build a shelter, paint your windows white, all that garbage. Having whitewashed windows is going to make one hell of a difference when a trillion tonnes of moon lands outside the house.

Kerry comes into the living room. She's got her mobile in one hand and a hankie in the other. She's crying. I tried to call my mum. I can't get a signal. I pull on the wine bottle, draining it. She's all alone, Kerry says. She won't know what to do.

There's nothing anyone can do, I say and get up and walk into the kitchen to get more wine. Thank fuck the bottles are screw top, I think. A waste of valuable seconds having to uncork the bastards.

I top up Kerry's half-filled glass. My hands have stopped shaking. I take the glass and the bottle back through to the living room. Kerry's perched at the edge of the couch, watching the TV.

We have to build a shelter, it says.

Where? I say. With what? The moon's going to obliterate everything and no amount of sheltering's going to help anything.

We should at least try.

Why? I ask. I hand her the glass of wine.

The telly says we should, Kerry says.

I feel drained. Why did this have to happen on a Friday? I say. Why not a fucking Sunday? Then there'd be the consolation of not having to go to fucking work on Monday.

The sound of car tyres screeching makes Kerry jump. What's that? She asks.

I go over to the window. John's car slaloms up the street, bashing into parked vehicles and driving through gardens. It comes to an abrupt halt when it ploughs into a lamp post.

To the west, obscured by houses, is a huge fire. I can see the smoke rising from the town a few miles away, see the reflection of flames on the underside of a few small clouds. John's car blows up.

What was that? Was that an explosion?

John's car.

Oh my God. He wasn't in it? Kerry gets up and comes over to the window but I draw the curtains. There's no need for her to see this, the town on fire that is. Didn't take too long for the rioting, I think. Fifteen minutes to live and people spend it by burning stuff.

Kerry slumps down on the couch. I stand in the middle of the living room and chug on the wine bottle.

Is that a good idea, she says, sipping at her glass.

Anything anyone on this planet does in the next five minutes is a good idea.

The television goes silent. It shows only static on its screen.

What's wrong with the telly? Kerry picks up the remote and tries other channels but finds only more silent static.

I think the moon's knocked out the satellites, I say. Can't be much longer now.

Kerry screams and throws her wine glass at the TV. Fuck! Fuck it! I don't want this to happen! She begins to cry uncontrollably. I switch the TV off and light the two candles that sit on the hearth.

The dinosaurs, she sobs. The asteroid that killed them. How did they die?

Horribly, I say. They died horribly.

Kerry stops crying. You're not fucking funny, she shouts. You're supposed to protect me! She comes over and hugs me.

I can't take any comfort in this gesture. I manoeuvre the wine bottle between us and drink as much as I can. Kerry sighs, takes the bottle from me and takes a few large mouthfuls.

I untangle myself and go to the kitchen. I pick out two bottles of wine from the box and pick up Kerry's cigarettes. No point in going into the garden to smoke now, I think as I light one. I go back to the living room with the lit cigarette dangling from my lips. I give one of the bottles and the cigarette packet to Kerry then sit on the couch.

The lights go out; there's no power. I hear Kerry's wine bottle thump against the floor. As my eyes adjust to the dim candlelight I can see her fumbling with the cigarette packet. She lights one and takes several deep puffs.

I take a few drags myself then pop the butt into an empty wine bottle. I open another bottle and drink as much as I can. I begin to cough, and spew up some wine. I fight the rest back down.

Kerry doesn't seem to mind that I've honked up on the couch; she's drinking greedily now herself.

I take the cigarette packet from Kerry and light another. I look at the cigarette, its white funnel of carcinogens. There probably isn't enough time to smoke all of it. I didn't get cancer, I say to Kerry. I open another bottle of wine. Didn't get liver shit either, I say.

Kerry's staring at one of the candles. Do you think it will hit us?

Dunno, I say. Does it matter? I suddenly have an urge to go and look out of the window but I realise I'm paralysed; I can't move my legs or raise myself up from my slumped position on the couch.

The flash of light is incredibly, unbelievably intense. I throw myself on to the floor, covering my head with my arms. Kerry's screaming abruptly stops.

I can't see; I feel about me for Kerry and call her name. I find a wine bottle instead.

Then there's an unearthly roaring and rumbling like the worst ever fairground ride. Things are crashing about me, falling picture frames and the bookcase. The windows shatter. The shaking becomes violent and I'm actually being lifted up and bounced off the floor until I can take it no more and begin to scream and the

Fran Baillie

At The Hinner-End

Aince a gallus limmer Eh mind o ye, skelpin roond the flair,
a strappin chiel, nooadays gey clappit-in. Ye yaist tae traips the toon
gittin fu an makkin collogue wi abdy; a callant, sae birkie an gleg,
blest wi the gift o the gab.

Bit snell winds o auld age blah an gaur banes loss thir jizz.
Time scrieves an scarts a brent broo,
taks awa the glent fae haff-blin ehs,
maks a cat's erse o a runklie mooth,
scunners, an laives a dwinin boady wantin;
maks ye pit claes on the wrangwyeroond an
hirple, weegletie-waggletie when ye wak an
forgit aathin.

Seldom noo, fae aneath aa this, oot keeks a glimmer o whit ye wirr;
mixter-maxter like a fireflaucht hingin ower a lochan, licht then daurk,
syne licht aince mair, bit nooadays maistly gaen back tae daurk.

Though, when lichtsomeness diz kittle ye, yer girns an thrawnness laive an
Eh git tae hear ye laffin, the roch pech o it dirlin up fae awa doon,
yer wee bit joshin hystin agin the shaddas thit hing aboot
gin lowsin time.

172

Pentin

Eh wiz pentin meh loaby wi gowden matt 'Sahara'
bombazed an trauchled, so tae feenish aff festish
Eh conjurt bein a traivler explorin vast Sudan an
Eh smoort the wah wi bylin desert sun.

Eh imagint puggelt geckos thit coodnae pit thir pahs doon,
syne they liftit twa at aince so thir feet werna blistert an
at cool wee oases whar yi got the freshest watter
wi rare lissum palms thit hid bra shady brainches,
the Bedouin hunkert doon, beildit mangst the dunes
an poored oot shoogree tea fae dinky, skinklin kettles
fae awa up heh, makkin muckle bubbles
tae weet thir drouthy thrapples an git a slakin drappie.

Unsneckit camels cooried, sunlicht baitin on thir hurdies;
a thae did wis argie-bargie an mak sic a boorach thit
amangst a the racket an the hale clamjamfry
eh cood hardly git meh haid roon pentin meh loaby…

Noo ehm feenisht wi 'Sahara' an it's aa gone affy quehit
an Ehm missin a meh freens fae far Sudan.

Fran Baillie

Musin

My Muse, tho' hamely in attire, may touch the heart – Robert Burns

Fae oot o a shrood o smirr, here's Ms Muse,
an aboot time tae; a doon-hauden sowl,
skulkin aboot, forjeskit; aye it the coo's erse,
yir trachlin up the road in claes o corbie-black.
Ae meenit Eh kin speh yi, wummin, syne yiv jinkit oota sicht,
skinklin in an oot like a staur; raid in the faiss
wi a wecht on yir shidders, swettin, girnin an
gittin meh hopes up forbye, yi bizum.

Yi bring a puckle o fantoosh ehdeas wi yi
thit pit mi in a boorach, bombaze mi;
stuff Eh've nae yaiss fir, stappit fou o haverin miths an aathin;
whitiver comes up yir humph, yi bletherin skite!

Noo, Eh'm no a greetin Teenie bit bring iz a wee buttie craic
thit's doon tae erth, naethin aboot merfowk an hoabgoblins,
bit ornary chiels like cats an doags; oads an ends
like sumthin eh fund when Eh pyked intae ma mither's bags
when Time pit er licht oot, or a wee buttie histry.

Bit lave the hehfallutin stuff thit's beyond mi ken, abuv mi haid,
thit gits mi birse up an laves mi disjaskit. Lave it fir sumdy
pan loaf thit chunters cut gless — a guid makar.
Bit, fir aa that... Eh'm sweir ti say,
 mibbee Eh shood hing in wi yi, dree mi ain weird,
 tak whit yi bring, yaze it an treh tae ging ad altiora.

174

John McMillan

For Jeanne Duval, Lover Of Baudelaire

Belle Creole, a feral muse were you
A moody cat about the poet's hearth
A fiery-adumbrated ingenue
The Persian rug your preferential berth

Colonial and scarcely francophone
You could not shrive yourself of your mystique
Dusk incarnate; hauteur in your bones
A petit patois, straight from Martinique

Manet records your eyes as purest jet
And gazing on the hidden world to come
Your dangling curls seditious spirochetes
The arm-rest of the *chaise* your Udu drum

They say you shared a scythe with Charles's *Fleurs*
But in that book your bold aspect endures

(Jeanne Duval died of syphilis, seemingly contracted from Charles Baudelaire, at the age of 42. Baudelaire's principal poetic work, Les Fleurs Du Mal (The Flowers of Evil) contains 12 poems inspired by Jeanne, known collectively as The Black Venus cycle.)

John McMillan

Before I Saw The Factor's Fees

I'm looking at
a riverfront apartment
quite affordable
ground level though,
so I suppose
there will be passing interest
from the burglars
and junkies
who frequent
the northern bank.
But I can count
on the cooperation of
the latter group at least —
they'll queue up
at my half-cracked
kitchen window
while I pour
runny honey down a
tilted Bowie knife
and let them,
mouths agape like
baby birds,
swallow an
eternal golden thread.

Finola Scott

We Are What We Eat

L ast week I went into a bookshop excited at the prospect of quiet browsing. I'm not a fan of e-reading. I'm into the whole sensory experience — holding the book, being the first to turn the pages. I love the smell of fresh print in the morning. So there I was in a bookshop, looking for a book. I wasn't looking for just any book but had quite specific requirements, as a friend had been diagnosed as a coeliac. I had to get a book with simple recipes, which would allow her to eat without fuss. Was that too much? Well, it seemed it was.

To reach the Cookery section I had to navigate a huge range of non-fiction. I wove a careful path through tables laden with 'Latest Best Sellers'. Celebrity autobiographies pulled at my coat, piles of Pert Pippa's Party Planner clamoured for attention. It was a shock that so many books were connected to TV programmes. Their Technicolor covers could have advertised a portrait gallery. Neil Oliver tossed his hair at the edge of a craggy cliff, Michael Portillo teetered on a railway platform clutching a worn red book.

At last, I arrived at the Cookbooks. I use the term loosely. You'd starve if you actually wanted to use these books to cook. Soft focus, soft porn, sofa books tried to seduce me. Close-up photography wooed me. Sparkling strawberries nestled in artfully arranged grass. Black puddings bled into béchamel, faggots fizzed in fat, full-colour centre-folds teased guzzling gourmets.

I looked in vain for recipes, detailed instructions, weights and measures. These books weren't mere instruction manuals. These books were to be savoured for themselves. They were no prelude to fine dining, but replacements. Their true homes weren't kitchen tables but coffee tables. It appears there's nothing people like doing more than browsing a cookbook. The irony is that they do this while absentmindedly munching fast food.

Cooking has become a spectator sport. There is now a TV Channel totally dedicated to food. It's easy to find, it's called the Food Channel. The programmes are, to say the least, varied. Some are studio based with various resident gurus teaching the art of pastry making while chatting to 'friends', most of whom are minor celebrities. These shows are often the best if you actually want to make something for tea. Others are more like travelogues, with 'famous' chefs eagerly following white robed figures down back alleys in Marrakech. We are breathlessly told, with a wink and nod, that the man is taking us to his third cousin's husband who is a renowned butcher. Soon

177

viewers are shown close up how the locals slaughter baby goats. The worst programmes are a sort of train-crash TV — you know you should look away but are mesmerised by the crassness. One such programme featured the narrator attempting to eat the most amount of food at one sitting. After watching entire cows roasted and basted the viewer was treated to close-ups of the presenter pushing half a rump, dripping with fat, into his gaping mouth. It was enough to put a Glaswegian off a pie supper.

A new breed of chefs has hijacked language. We no longer burn food but 'caramelise' it, gravy becomes 'jus', food isn't fried but 'seared'. Food has been redefined. Many chefs specialise in deconstructing food. Much of this harks back with an ironic wink to earlier, more humble ways of cooking. The simple dish of boiled egg and toast soldiers is probably the subject of a doctoral thesis somewhere. Other chefs specialise in dissembling. They dumb down the language refusing to use anything that might be mistaken for a technical term. One such cheery London chef instructs us to 'bosh in a big glug of local plonk'. He calls his burgers 'cheeky chappies' and encourages us to cook a three course meal in 8 minutes, as if existence were a race. I wistfully think back to Marguerite Patten and her one pot Mediterranean meals in a gentle hour. The chefs I find most difficult are those who seem to have forgotten the very basic purpose of food. Molten sugar, for these alchemists, is something used to spin a golden cage to corral handmade ice-cream. Whether food is edible seems to be beside the point. The more outrageous the dish the more adulation garnered. Tripe biscuits are served with cacao foam, floating in a sea of taramasalata broth. The more obscure the ingredient the better.

The covers of many books featured TV chefs who have been elevated to sainthood. You know the people I mean. 'Celebrity Chefs' they are called. I ask you. The sad thing is that I recognised many names. One cook specialised in taking us back to where food is grown. In one of his programmes I watched open mouthed as he instructed his guests in the art of building a smoke house. Windswept city types stood about a huge manicured garden, holding rusted bits of corrugated iron, hanging on his every word. It appears kippers are only worth eating if you've smoked them yourself. Later in the same series, he instructed us in the art of eating on the cheap. He waxed lyrical about quail — the eggs and the actual birds. I didn't quite catch what was to be done with the carcass. I'm sure it wasn't anything to do with soup, but suspect a jelly was to be made from the tiny bones. What kind of custard would go with that? The most well-known face grinning from the shelves was a woman's. We all know her; she's the food writer for those who feel guilty about eating. Licking a spoon, she'll reassure you that calories are a decadent must. You'll feel like a killjoy if you count the carbohydrates or the cost. I thought I'd caught my partner watching porn when I walked in on him enjoying her show. Spatulas will never be the same. Whipping, folding, smoothing and spreading are her specialities. Me? I mostly stir.

What of the cookbook for my friend? Honestly, it was easier just to look up the internet.

Apples

First, the radio died.
Accents broke like bee hives
splintering between Midas-stroked gardens.
Streams were gargled in bridge mouth-holes
and cow bellies flattened twigs, branches, grass and soil.
Tractors, fluent in interfering rocks,
moved you like nostalgia
towards the clock of earliest years;
     thorns prickling bare legs
     and the blood-red leaves
     of the Scottish borders.

The endless hedgerows and sheep
were like soldiers guarding a fortress
where the dead could sleep in peace.
Dark anchors of flowers made heartbeats of land;
sleeves of graveyards
where only moon feet dared to tread in the balm of twilight.
Your own feet, pale and light then,
feverishly following a local boy
who smelt of apples and cinnamon,
     tasted of watermelon;
     adrenaline.

Stephen Watt

This lane. Yes, this lane's bones
sing, smile, serenade in the shadows of a place once known to you.
The ashes of ghosts blow from the steps,
while curious birds in their nests
gesture and babble when the brass handle strikes the door.
Footsteps on floorboards come close.
A ginger tom pulls a face at the window
     and just before you start to feel vulnerable,
     the unmistakable scent of apples
     settles your pulse; regenerates hope.

First prize winner of the inaugural Federation of Writers (Scotland) poetry competition in 2013.

John Wyllie

A Journey Through Finland

He and she speed mile after mile
through twilight's black gaps
and dim, white, forever forest.
Sitting together,
he and she cut by culture
and the cold side of love;
listening to long trails of tribal speech.
The bus crunches between them
and pristine cracks of snow
on dark gutters of straight road.

Many trees bow right over
meeting early death and winter,
caught with their leaves still on
in the dripping grip of snow;
with the creak of cracking wood
kissing the ground.
They dust white peppered meadows
that slash dark surrounding forest.

John Wyllie

Passengers nod in rattling dreams
or talk soft Suomi vowels.
They pass a few last opaque wooden houses,
standing distilled
in denuded bones of land.
She and he rushing through woods
big enough to fill a thousand postcards.
She and Nature
with their wild look
in this twilight country.

He steams the window with his breath
and writes in clean, remote English:
'I love you still'.
She smiles,
but far into the dim bus
and out,
through layers of shaking glass
in to the dark lands.

Joint second prize winner of the Federation of Writers (Scotland) poetry competition in 2013.

John Wyllie

The Comin

The Earth is like a skin stretched on bane,
afore the croon o' May.
A' gurlie wi caws o' corbies an spurdies,
each ta his ane.
Bowed are the birks and spread'n the doo-dokens,
deep in the fludder and muck o' last year;
awaitin aye moment ta burst their stickie buds,
ta unfold their leafy honds afore a timmerous sun.

Doon in the fracklin windy wid,
flour heeds come tip-toein through feckless licht.
The emerant skin o' life stands clathed in a sweet goun:
a bonny shrood growin oor the deed o' winter.
This incarnit velvous creature
wheasels an swashes across the hallowed groond;
skirlin and squakin like ony gaspin gubbie,
demandin to be fed,
the whirligig flees an clock-leddys fast comin.

This newborn spring:
a splutter o' blue lift and a spirk o' chameleon carpet;
a garden unguarded, gallopin awa,
a dreeple o' bricht glowmuins inta the peppery nichts.
Nay sour at the passin o' the auld yin:
but graced and gallus, reid nakit as a wean in warmth,
and aye wis greetin fir the lang summer days, yet ta come.

Joint second prize winner of the Federation of Writers (Scotland) poetry competition in 2013.

Kay Ritchie

Early Sunshine

Madrid is miserable in March and I'm
wound tight in grey melancholia and a medley of wools.

From the window of the bus I watch
this icy wind scratch at wintry skies as
we travel south towards spring.

In Seville I peel off layers. Drop them
like the bitter sweet oranges that litter streets in autumn.
That smell of fragrant marmalade.

Suddenly and at last — the Algarve, the Atlantic and
tangled by the roadside, wild flowers in
scattered skeins of green. Purple. Crimson. Yellow.

Then Faro. Far from el frio. And, as if wool has been pulled from
my freezing ears, I hear the song of blackbirds, swifts, swallows.
Giddy with spring, I step from the bus

into the blue. It is that time when dark and light knit together perfectly.
Tomorrow I will unwind, once more, with you.

Third prize winner of the inaugural Federation of Writers (Scotland) poetry competition in 2013.

Christmas Spirits

The young carer steered Mary through the doorway and into the lounge.
"Mary, I'm going to leave you in here, with Agnes."

The thick carpet caught the soft sole of Mary's shoe and she stumbled, knocking into the girl who held her arm. "Bloody shoes. I told you to get my slippers! No one *ever* listens to me. It's like I don't bloody well exist."

A sharp intake of breath was the only answer given.

The Larches advertised exceptional care, with a price tag to match.

Two designated armchairs had been set in the bay window, allowing a view of the grounds, in isolation from the day room where everyone else gathered. The outlook was of little interest, across the gravel drive, the lawn and to the woods beyond. The sky was pale with winter chill and the moon hovered, misplaced, waiting for dusk.

Inside Agnes sat alone by the window in the empty room. She too was misplaced and waiting. A vague sour scent hung around her, tainting her charm. Her colours — muted greys and pink — matched her soft manner. Her eyes never left the view but she spoke, very softly in acknowledgment, as a shadow moved in and Mary was seated in the empty chair at her side.

"Ah isn't it so nice to see the sun out, so nice."

Mary sat carefully, pulled the cushion forward, plumped it vigorously on her knee, and placed it at a better angle behind her back. She looked officious, in her smart navy trousers and matching blazer. A chiffon scarf hung loose at her neck, softening the formality of her outfit. She fussed over her handbag and eventually squeezed it between herself and the side of the seat. Her slight figure barely filled the chair.

"What did you say? My son? I don't think I'll see my son today. He's abroad you know — the bugger!" She returned to her handbag, snapped it open and pulled out an envelope. "The last time I saw him he was wearing his uniform... I do like to see a man in uniform, buttons polished, shoes glinting and a hat... Charlie wore his with a slight tilt. Look." She thrust a photograph at Agnes. "Bloody smart, eh! I got a salute and he marched across the tarmac and onto the plane — and then he was gone. Like father like son!" The envelope lay on her lap and she studied her hands, then pulled a small white handkerchief from her left sleeve, folded it neatly once and replaced it into her right sleeve. "Robert was... Well, Robert! I married his uniform. He was a useless bugger. In the end he was just a bloody useless old bugger."

186

A radio played next door and the dull drone of voices drifted through. A bell rang in the distance and the hurry of footsteps followed.

Agnes said, "That's nice... Oh look — a car coming. I can hear it on the gravel. I wonder who that is." She made no sign of having heard Mary's tale; the photograph, held in her hand, was ignored. She had seen a car arrive. Now it was out of her line of sight, at the front door. The blanket hid her stiffened knees.

Mary stood up and leaned forward, watching out of the window as the taxi stopped.

"It's that handsome man I saw yesterday. Checking out the joint, I'll bet! He's brought a suitcase. I do hope he's not going to carry that himself. He can hardly lift it. Oh, here comes Dudley, dopey as ever... He's on drugs, you know. You watch his eyes — shifty — hunted." She turned to make sure Agnes heard that damning comment.

Agnes avoided her glance. Instead she changed the subject. In her quiet voice she said, "That's nice. Have they finished that Christmas tree yet? The lights were still off when I saw it last night. It's very small. I don't know why they don't get one from the woods. It's not as if anyone else would know. That's what we used to do. At home... First job for the boys. Go and find a tree, cut it down and bring it up to the house. John did all that really — the boys tried to help. He wouldn't let the boys use the saw. Paranoid — that's what the boys called him. It was the same with the guns. Only one key. He had rules... I do like a tree, a real tree. My sister — Jean — she just has a plastic one. No fun in that. Plastic! It's not as if she doesn't have room for a real one. She doesn't like the mess — any mess. She didn't like the boy's mess. So we didn't visit."

Mary spoke again. "Charlie — he always wanted to be a soldier. Even from a toddler he ran around with guns, shooting everything. I knew. I knew he would be a soldier." She let her head drop.

"That's nice... Listen — Christmas carols?" Agnes's mind drifted to the past. "I wonder what happened to my box of decorations... Spring Mains, that was the farm. We had the big house. Just right for a family — four boys and my husband, John. All my babies — that was what I always said — endless sleepless nights. Even now you know! I bet one of my boys took the box. My special fairy. And a tiny glass trumpet... I loved them."

Agnes looked towards her companion for the first time, but Mary's eyes were on her hands again.

187

"Not much of a family. Only boys. Incomplete." Mary let a smile sweep momentarily across her face. She reached for her bag again, clicked it open and searched through the contents. A small, grubby piece of paper was carefully taken out. Letting the bag slip back onto the seat, she concentrated on this treasure and opened it to lie flat on her knees. Another smile set her face as she studied the childish drawing. Across the bottom it said *MY MUMMY BY NICHOLA 1959*. The memory enclosed her.

Sometime later Mary returned this prize to her bag, and the envelope with the pictures slid to the floor. "Oh Charlie!" She shook her head and worry darkened her eyes as she picked it up. "I told him, just avoid a bullet! I don't want an early morning visit from a policeman. Have you ever had an early morning visit from a bloody policeman?"

Agnes dropped her eyelids and said nothing. Her chin wobbled once and her lips tightened. A handkerchief held in her hand took her attention and she twisted it tight. Then she turned her head away as a private tear slipped down her cheek. She stared unseeing at the curtains, tension gripping her shoulders.

"Have you?" repeated Mary. "I have. *The* most terrifying thing. Out of the night, darkness and then the flicker of blue across the ceiling. Stunned into — into — just, bloody hell! Charlie! Missing! I was so frightened!" Her voice whispered emotion. "Charlie, my baby! But — they found him — wounded but alive..." She grabbed the photograph back from Agnes and held it tight against her chest. "Just don't say *that's nice*!"

Agnes moved her lips and a whisper escaped: "The police, yes. The police came, yes." Her eyes glazed and she sat like stone.

Mary continued, "And he's back out there again. Says he can't live without the army now. Good money. Good life — he says."

A murmur came from Agnes, "The court was worse. Everyone knew. Guilty... I knew he was guilty. You don't live with a man for twenty years and not know when he's lying." Her voice was thin, monotone. "Twenty years, that's what he got. And me — another twenty years. Why did he want so much money?" She clutched her handkerchief.

"What are you saying? How many years? Well, Robert was the same, twenty years. He came home bloody paralysed. Hospital first — took a long time to get him home. I remember that Christmas. He couldn't do anything. He was like a stranger — outer space — he just sat in the front room. Didn't want to go anywhere! Said he had dreamed of our front room. That was all he wanted. And we just lived round about him. The kids opened his presents.

They were so excited. *They* didn't mind if he just sat. It was me, I was just so cross, Mrs Bloody Well Angry. And then they sent an ambulance and took him back. More operations! I wouldn't have minded, but none of them worked. Bedridden. Bloody bedridden!"

After a brief silence, Agnes said, "That's nice! It would have been nice if John had come home — especially for Christmas. We had to sort visits around everything else. And — no one wanted to go, especially me! A cardboard cut-out would have been fine. Then his presence could have mattered, younger, innocent, Dad, and honest... No guilt, no shame, no hate." Her voice dropped away.

Mary spoke, her voice thick. "Guilt! That wears you out, too. Guilt! It stops you from sleeping. I was frightened to think about what I really wanted. No-one asked what I thought. He was just coming home." She reached out to Agnes, letting her hand brush the papery skin of her cheek as she spoke. "And I knew he loved us so much. That was why he just wanted to be there."

"That's really nice, dear. And I know John loved me. Too much, probably. He thought money was important. And I guess that's why the guilt lives on. I never told him..." Her sadness overflowed, unhindered now.

Mary held her hand tight. "In my heart, when I dared to think, I knew I didn't want him back. I was frightened. I just saw him... Another baby and... I gave them up after Nicola died. Three! Just bloody three years old!" The tears that had pooled in her eyes spilt with every blink. She stared out over the grounds.

They sat together, comfortable in their closeness, letting their tears dry.

"And for every Christmas, for every picture of Christmas, I've had this ache," said Agnes presently. She put her fingers round the wizened hand of her companion and tried a smile.

"Do you know, I feel better than I have done in years?" Mary smiled back.

"Do you think that new resident could do with some of our cheer?" Their uncontrolled laughter echoed into the hall.

"I'm dreaming of a black Christmas from the ones I used to know..." Mary's voice, high, splintered.

Two nurses watched from the door before marching in. A whisper passed between them: "I don't believe it. Those two are actually talking — and laughing, look!"

"It must be a Christmas spirit... Now! Ladies, enough of your jokes. It's almost tea time. Agnes, come on, you'll need to change those pants."

The wheelchair was moved close and Agnes hobbled over, supported by the young nurse.

As they accelerated across the main hall, Agnes said, "Nurse, can I sit with her at dinner? With Mary? And — any chance that new chap might join us?"

"Agnes! You'll be asking for wine next," the nurse answered. "I didn't know you and Mary were friends. There *is* a new member, arrived this afternoon — Mr Harrison."

"Oh? Not Rex, I don't suppose!"